Est. 1968 Fax No. (24 hrs): 01543 473234	**J. WELS** P.O. Box 150, Burto Staffs DE13 Callers by appointment only a

COINS FOR SALE

GOLD COINS

James I Laurel S.2638B GVF+ **£450**
James I ¼ Laurel GVF+ **£225**
Charles I Unite GVF+ S.2693A **£450**
Henry VII Angel S.2183 GVF **£395**
1893 £5 A/UNC. Very rare **£795**
1902 MP £5 GEM FDC **£650**
1937 Pr. £5 GEM FDC **£695**

£2 PIECES

1887 £2 BU GEM **£325**
1902 £2 GEM FDC **£350**
1902 MP £2 GEM FDC **£325**
1937 Pr. £2 FDC **£325**
1983 Pr. £2 FDC Orig. Box............... **£190**
1986 Pr. £2 FDC Orig. Box............... **£190**
1986 Pr. £2 FDC **£175**
1986 Pr. £2 FDC **£175**
1987 Pr. £2 FDC Orig. Box............... **£195**
1888 Pr. £2 FDC Orig. Box............... **£195**
1989 £2 FDC Orig. Box **£200**

5 GUINEAS, 2 GUINEAS, Etc.

1700 5 Gn. GVF Rare **£1500**
1768 Gn. Nice VF Rare.................... **£160**
1772 Gn. GVF+ **£175**
1774 Gn. NVF **£110**
1776 Gn. GVF................................. **£150**
1777 Gn. NVF **£110**
1777 Gn. GF **£100**
1778 Gn. GF **£100**
1784 Gn. VF **£120**

1787 Gn. BU **£350**
1789 Gn. VF **£115**
1798 Gn. BU GEM **£275**
1785 ½ Gn. BU Rare **£225**
1803 ⅓ Gn. NVF/VF **£45**
1804 ⅓ Gn. GVF **£55**
1804 ⅓ Gn. VF **£48**
1808 ⅓ Gn. VF **£48**
1810 ⅓ Gn. BU................................. **£100**
1718 ¼ Gn. GVF+ **£90**

SOVEREIGNS

1836 EF.. **£250**
1841 Fine Extremely rare................. **£395**
1886 M EF St. Geo. **£75**
1886 M St. Geo. A/UNC.................... **£90**
1889 S BU **£100**
1902 MP UNC................................... **£120**
1909 C EF Very rare **£140**
1911 S BU **£75**
1911 L ABU **£70**
1919 P BU **£80**
1925 M BU Rare **£120**
1927 SA BU **£85**
1929 SA BU GEM **£85**
1931 SA BU **£80**
1931 SA BU GEM **£85**
1931 P BU GEM **£85**
1932 SA BU GEM Rare...................... **£95**
1932 SA FDC................................... **£100**
1937 Pr. GEM FDC Extremely rare ... **£395**

**ABOVE IS A SMALL SELECTION FROM OUR LARGE STOCK OF
ENGLISH AND FOREIGN GOLD COINS. WE CAN ALSO OFFER YOU ON
OUR MONTHLY SALES LIST A VERY WIDE RANGE OF ENGLISH SILVER,
COPPER COINS, GOLD AND SILVER PROOF SETS
AT COMPETITIVE PRICES.**

**IF YOU WOULD LIKE TO RECEIVE MY FREE MONTHLY SALES LIST
PLEASE WRITE, TELEPHONE OR FAX ME**

4

COINS *International*

WANT TO BUY

BRITISH SILVER COINS	COLLECTIONS OR SINGLE ITEMS. CROWNS – DOUBLE FLORINS – HALF CROWNS – FLORINS – SHILLINGS – SIXPENCES – GROATS – THREEPENCES – THREE HALF PENCES – MAUNDY SETS ETC.
GOLD & BULLION COINS	£5 AND £2 PIECES – SOVEREIGNS – HALF SOVEREIGNS – GUINEAS – HALF GUINEAS AND FRACTIONAL GUINEAS. KRUGERRANDS – MAPLE LEAFS – BRITANNIAS ETC. ALL FOREIGN AND COMMONWEALTH GOLD COINS.
PROOF SETS & CROWNS	ALL BRITISH – COMMONWEALTH AND FOREIGN ISSUES.
WAR MEDALS, ORDERS & DECORATIONS	ALL BRITISH – COMMONWEALTH AND FOREIGN.
SILVER & GOLD MEDALLIONS	BY PINCHES – HALLMARK – POBJOY – BIRMINGHAM MINT – FRANKLIN MINT ETC. PRIVATE AND OTHER ISSUES. ALSO POSTAGE STAMP REPLICAS.
PRE 1947 BRITISH SILVER COINS	IN ANY CONDITION. ALSO FOREIGN SILVER COINS OF ANY DATE.
COPPER & BRONZE COINS	BRITISH AND COMMONWEALTH EF TO MINT CONDITION. SINGLE COINS OR COLLECTIONS.
	BULK LOTS – ACCUMULATIONS – COLLECTIONS. ANY ARTICLES IN GOLD OR SILVER – WATCHES – JEWELLERY – CHAINS – RINGS – BRACELETS – SILVER CUTLERY – CANDLE STICKS AND TEA SERVICES ETC. (DAMAGED OR UNDAMAGED).
ACCESSORIES	FULL RANGE OF COIN ACCESSORIES AND LINDNER PRODUCTS. PHONE OR WRITE FOR LEAFLET AND CATALOGUE.

1 & 2 MELBOURNE STREET, LEEDS LS2 7PS.
TEL: LEEDS (0113) 2434230.
FAX: (0113) 2345544.
CALLERS WELCOME – OPEN MON-FRI 9am-5pm.

Gold, silver, copper, bronze.
Celtic, Saxon, Hammered, Milled.

For over 27 years Dolphin Coins have helped collectors of English coins acquire the very best - no matter what field they collect.

BRITISH COINS MARKET VALUES

CONTENTS

Executive Editor:
Richard West

Group Advertisement Manager:
Gary Ashburn

Publishing Director:
Peter Warwick

Published by:
Link House
Magazines Ltd
Link House
Dingwall Avenue
Croydon CR9 2TA
Tel: 0181 686 2599
Fax: 0181 781 6044

Distributed by:
USM Distribution Ltd
85-86 Newman Street
London W1P 3LD
Tel: 0171 396 8000
Fax: 0171 392 8002

ISBN 0-86296-131-9

A LINK HOUSE ANNUAL

Market Trends

WE have been monitoring the domestic coin market in these pages for over 30 years and it is our opinion that the current situation is very healthy indeed. Headed by the BNTA we have a strong force of good professional dealers, excellent catalogues and many good and informative books to support the subject. What a difference from the days when we started out.

In the past twelve months we have seen new collectors appearing on the scene, and there is no doubt that London continues to be the world centre for coins. There seem to have been so many important auctions in London and with the constant competition between Spink and Sotheby, Baldwin, Bonham's, Glendining and Dix and Webb, it makes for a lively scenario. At any major London auction you will find among the bidders, representatives from many of the important coin firms from around the globe.

On these pages though we concentrate only on the domestic material covered by our catalogue section later on, and it has become our tradition to look at each of the main series.

Ancient British

In the early 70s British Celtic coins attracted strong prices and then came a slump, partly because of stolen hoards and worries about forgery. That is well behind us now and after a good twenty years of being comparatively undervalued, British Celtic coins continue to rise gradually and steadily in price as new collectors continue to discover the hitherto hidden pleasure potential of this fascinating and complex series. Chris Rudd, the only dealer that deals only Celtic, reports that very fine dynastic bronze, unpublished silver and extremely rare gold staters are achieving the highest figures, both at auction and in fixed price catalogues. We anticipate that the British Celtic market will be further stimulated in 1997 with the recent publication of two excellent new books: Dr Philip de Jersey's *Celtic Coinage in Britain* (Shire Archaeology, £4.99) and Richard Hobbs' *British Iron Age Coins in the British Museum* (British Museum Press, £40).

This superb Gallo-Belgic Goddess gold stater was sold by Chris Rudd for £3,000 in August 1996

This unpublished Chichester Chariot Wheel Silver unit was sold by Chris Rudd for £550 in May 1966

English Hammered Gold

In this series we find many of the famous denominations, for example the noble, the angel, the sovereign (depicting the portrait of the monarch enthroned and facing the viewer), and so on. There are many beautiful designs to be found here, some in Gothic style.

A world record price of £159,500 at Spink for this Henry III gold penny

The main story of the year belongs to Spink with the world record price of £159,500 (includes premium), paid for a Henry III gold penny in July 1996. It was last offered for sale by auction by the same company in 1993 and failed to attract a bid. What a different story this time round, and it only emphasises the strength of today's market.

Across the board good quality hammered gold pieces are on the rise and they have been given a further boost in interest by the superb catalogue of the Schneider collection (the best private collection ever assembled) produced by Spink for only £60. A must for all serious collectors!

Milled Gold

It is a similar story here with very strong prices being paid for EF+ coins. But where is all the material? We cannot remember a time when there was such a dearth of top quality gold coins. Where are those choice little guineas, and five guineas? Are they being hoarded for a rainy day when we have a possible change of government? It is worth remembering that the market for these pieces has traditionally always been stronger during the term of a Labour Government, so maybe collectors are holding on to see what happens.

Hammered Silver

This is the largest area in the whole British series, starting with the small stubby sceats of the Anglo-Saxon period, and ending with the often badly struck hammered coins of Charles II. There are many themes for the new collectors; some will find the penny stimulating, while others collect groats, testoons, sixpences, and so on.

This seems to be the year when the crown returned to form, as we predicted in these pages last year. This was underlined by the Spink sale of the Mantegazza collection in March 1996. It really did exceed all expectations with 187 lots being quickly sold to an absorbed packed saleroom. It was noticeable too that the coins were bought by American, Dutch and Japanese bidders as well as domestic ones, demonstrating the international demand for these pieces.

Milled Silver

This is traditionally the area which attracts the most interest from domestic dealers and it has proved consistently stable. There is always a demand for top quality material and dealers in the know, both here and in the USA, can place the choice coins instantly. It was again noticeable how well the milled sold in the Mantegazza auction.

In our opinion too, Coincraft's *Standard Catalogue of English and UK coins*, new out last year, because of its instant popularity with the international coin trade, has been quite influential in stimulating this market. It will be interesting to see how their prices will change in the new edition this year; certainly in CMV we have made many changes.

This copper untrimmed strip of two Richmond farthings sold for £650 in 1996

Copper and Bronze

Each year we comment on the lack of good material, and so it continues. There is no big auction listing, or indeed in-depth dealer's list (although Colin Cooke of Manchester produces very good lists of farthings regularly), and this used to be one of the hottest areas of collecting during the change-checking boom of the 1960s. Is it because the coins deteriorate over the years if not carefully handled? This can happen particularly if kept in plastic wallets or envelopes (read our section on Keeping Your Coins). However, it is a wonderful area to collect: as a newcomer go and buy a copy of Peck's superb *British Museum Catalogue* (see Some Useful Books) and a whole new world will open up.

Scottish Coins

This very attractive series appeals particularly to those who spend a lot of time with purely English coins, since the designs of the Scottish pieces are so different, often reflecting a continental influence. Many of the denominations, too, are particularly Scottish, for example merks, bawbees, bodies, turners and sword dollars.

There are quite a number of new collectors emerging for Scottish material, and it is noticeable how good coins have quickly gone to ground.

We feel that it is an area where prices will continue to rise dramatically, and we have noticed how few decent Scottish coins there are in dealers trays these days, and as far as we know, there are no major auctions on the horizon either.

Irish Coins

The market in Ireland now is stronger than it has been for many years. There is competition in the area of coin shows between Peter Sheen (held last May) and Ian Whyte's (held in conjunction with the Irish Numismatic Society last March).

It is particularly pleasing to see the renaissance of the Irish Numismatic Society, which was a very influential body during the 60s and 70s.

Incidentally, as with the Scottish and Anglo-Gallic series, COINS MARKET VALUES offers the only up-to-date guide to prices.

Anglo-Gallic Coins

It is noticeable that at present the demand for Anglo-Gallic material is small but enthusiastic. It appears that there is a small number of aficionados around the world, and when they need a coin the price is strong, but there is no in depth support to buy numbers of these pieces. Dealers' lists usually only contain a sprinkling of material, and certainly silver and base metal coins seem to have largely dried up. (Patrick Finn aims to produce one good in-depth list every year). Ironically there were 17 gold pieces in the famous Strauss sale and yet arguably that was the least competitive part of the auction with prices on the low side.

The peak of the market remains the sale of the Elias collection in 1990, and all newcomers to the series must obtain the catalogue, which is still available from Spink.

Some Useful Books

Here is a small selection of books dealing with coins which are covered in COINS MARKET VALUES. Included are the prices you can expect to pay; some of the books are now out of print, but can still often be obtained second-hand (indicated in the list by SH).

Bateson, D. Scottish Coins (Shire publications Ltd, 1987). **£1.75.**

Besly, E. Coins and Medals of the English Civil War (1991). **£18.50.**

Blunt, C.E., Stewart, B.H.I.H., Lyon, C.S.S. Coinage in Tenth Century England 1989. **£60.**

Boon, G. Welsh Hoards 1979-1981 (1986). **£28.**

Boon, G. Coins of the Anarchy 1135-1154. 1988. **£4.**

Brand, J.D. Periodic Change of Type in the Anglo-Saxon and Norman Periods (1984). **£3.**

British Academy (Publisher) Sylloge of Coins of The British Isles. 44 volumes mostly in print, available individually. [See list on p.20]

Brooke, G.C. English Coins (Reprint edition, London 1966). **£12.**

Challis, C. A new History of the Royal Mint, 1992. **£95.**

Coincraft's Standard Catalogue of English and UK Coins, 1966. **£19.50.**

Cunliffe, B. and Miles, D. Aspects of the Iron Age in Central Southern Britain (Oxford 1984) for background reading. **£30.**

Dolley, M. Viking Coins in the Danelaw and Dublin (London 1965). **SH.**

Dolley, M. Anglo-Saxon Pennies (Reprint, London 1970). **SH.**

Dolley, M. The Norman Conquest and English Coinage (London 1966). **£2.**

Dowle, A. and Finn, P. The Guide Book to the Coinage of Ireland (London 1969). **SH.**

Elias, E.R.D. The Anglo-Gallic Coins (Paris/London 1984). **£20.**

Freeman, A. The Moneyer and the Mint in the Reign of Edward the Confessor 1042-1066. 2 parts (1985). **£40.**

Gouby, Michael. The British Bronze Penny (1986). **£19.95.**

Grueber, H.A. Handbook of the Coins of Great Britain and Ireland (Revised edition London 1970). **SH.**

Jonsson, K. The New Era. The Reformation of the late Anglo-Saxon Coinage (1987). **£25.**

Linecar, H.W.A. British Coin Designs and Designers (London 1977). **SH.**

Manville, H.E and Robertson, T.J. British Numismatic Auction Catalogues, 1710-1984 (1986). **£25.**

Manville, H.E., Numismatic guide to British and Irish periodicals 1731-1991. Part 1. (Archaeological.) **£60.**

Mays, M. (Editor). Celtic Coinage: Britain and Beyond. BAR Series 222 1992. **£32.**

McCammon, A.L.T. Currencies of the Anglo-Norman Isles (London 1984). **£25.** Supplement with much new information **£8.**

North, J.J. English Hammered Coins Two volumes. Volume 1; **£35;** and Volume 2, **£30.**

North, J.J. and Preston-Morley, P.J. The John G. Brooker Collection – Coins of Charles I (Sylloge of Coins of the British Isles, Number 33). **£19.50.**

O'Sullivan, W. The Earliest Anglo-Irish Coinage (second edition, Dublin 1964). **SH.**

Peck, C.W. English Copper, Tin and Bronze Coins in the British Museum 1558-1958 (London 1960). **SH.**

Pridmore, F. The Coins of the British Commonwealth of Nations: 1 – European Territories (London 1960). **SH.**

Rayner, P.A. *English Silver Coins Since 1649,* 1992. **£19.95.**

Robinson, B. Silver Pennies and Linen Towels: The Story of The Royal Maundy (1991). **£29.95.**

Seaby's. Standard Catalogue of British Coins, 32nd edition. **£12.95.**

Spink and Son (Publishers), Milled Coinage of England 1662-1946 (1958) reprinted **£5.**

Stewart, I.H. The Scottish Coinage (Second edition, London 1967). **SH.**

Sutherland, C.H.V. English Coinage 600-1900 (London 1973). **SH.**

Thompson, J.D.A. Inventory of British Coin Hoards AD 600-1500 (London 1956). **SH.**

Van Arsdell, R.D. Celtic Coinage of Britain (London 1989) **£40.**

Withers, P. and B. British Coin Weights. **£95.**

Woodhead, P. The Herbert Schneider Collection of English Gold Coins. Part 1. Henry III – Elizabeth I. **£60.**

Wren, C.R. The Voided Long Cross Coinage 1247-1279, 1993. **£9.**

Wren, C.R. The Short Cross Coinage 1180-1247. 1992. **£8.75.**

Abbreviations and Terms
used in the Market Price Guide Section

* — Asterisks against some dates indicate that no firm prices were available at the time of going to press.

2mm — P of PENNY is 2mm from trident. On other 1895 pennies the space between is only 1mm.

AE — numismatic symbol for copper or copper alloys.

Arabic 1, Roman I — varieties of the 1 in 1887.

Arcs — decorative border of arcs which vary in number.

B (on William III coins) — minted at Bristol.

1866 shilling lettered BBITANNIAR in error

BBITANNIAR — lettering error.

Bank of England — this issued overstruck Spanish dollars for currency use in Britain 1804-1811.

black — farthings 1897-1918, artificially darkened to avoid confusion with half sovereigns.

brit — lettering error.

B. Unc, BU — Brilliant Uncirculated condition.

C (on milled gold coins) — minted at Ottawa (Canada).

C (on William III coins) — minted at Chester.

close colon — colon close to DEF.

crosslet 4 — having upper and lower serifs to horizontal bar of 4 (see plain 4).

cu-ni — cupro-nickel.

dashes (thus —) following dates in the price list indicate that some particular characteristic of a coin is the same as that last described. Two dashes mean that two characters are repeated, and so on.

debased — in 1920 the silver fineness in British coins was debased from .925 to .500.

diag — diagonal.

'Dorrien and Magens' — issue of shillings by a group of bankers. Suppressed on the day of issue.

DRITANNIAR — lettering error.

E (on William III coins) — minted at Exeter.

E, E* (on Queen Anne coins) — minted at Edinburgh.

Edin — Edinburgh.

EEC — European Economic Community.

EF (over price column) — Extremely Fine condition.

E.I.C. — East India Co (supplier of metal).

Elephant and castle

eleph, eleph & castle — elephant or elephant and castle provenance mark (below the bust) taken from the badge of the African ('Guinea') Company, which imported the metal for the coins.

Eng — English shilling. In 1937, English and Scottish versions of the shilling were introduced. English versions: lion standing on crown (1937-51); three leopards on a shield (1953-66).

exergue — segment below main design, usually containing the date.

On this penny the exergue is the area containing the date

ext — extremely.

F — face value only.

F (over price column) — Fine condition.

(F) — forgeries exist of these pieces. In some cases the forgeries are complete fakes, in others where the date is rare the date of a common coin has been altered. Collectors are advised to be very cautious when buying any of these coins.

Fair — rather worn condition.

Fantasies — non-currency items, often just produced for the benefit of collectors.

far colon — colon farther from DEF than in close colon variety.

FDC — Fleur de coin. A term used to describe coins in perfect mint condition, with no flaws, scratches or other marks.

fig(s) — figure(s).

fillet — hair band.

flan — blank for a coin or medal.

GEOE — lettering error.

Florin of Victoria with the design in the Gothic style

Gothic — Victorian coins featuring Gothic-style portrait and lettering.

guinea head — die used for obverse of guinea.

H — mintmark of The Mint, Birmingham, Ltd.

hd — head.

hp, harp (early, ord etc.) — varieties of the Irish harp on reverse.

hearts — motif in top RH corner of Hanoverian shield on reverse.

illust — illustration, or illustrated.

im — initial mark.

inc, incuse — incised, sunk in.

inv — inverted.

JH — Jubilee Head.

The Jubilee Head was introduced on the coinage in 1887 to mark Victoria's Golden Jubilee

KN — mintmark of the Kings Norton Metal Co Ltd.

L.C.W. — initials of Leonard Charles Wyon, engraver.

lge — large.

LIMA — coins bearing this word were struck from bullion captured by British ships from foreign vessels carrying South American treasure, some of which may have come from Peru (capital Lima).

A

B

1902 pennies showing the low horizon variety (A) and the normal horizon (B)

low horizon — on normal coins the horizon meets the point where Britannia's left leg crosses behind the right. On this variety the horizon is lower.

LVIII etc — regnal year in Roman numerals on the edge.

matt — type of proof without mirror-like finish.

M (on gold coins) — minted at Melbourne (Australia).

'military' — popular name for the 1813 guinea struck for the payment of troops fighting in the Napoleonic Wars.

mm — mintmark.

Mod eff — modified effigy of George V.

mule — coin struck from wrongly paired dies.

N (on William III coins) — minted at Norwich.

William III shilling with N (for Norwich mint) below the bust

no. — number.

obv — obverse, usually the 'head' side of a coin.

OH — Old Head.

ord — ordinary.

OT — ornamental trident.

P (on gold coins) — minted at Perth (Australia).

pattern — trial piece not issued for currency.

piedfort — a coin which has been specially struck on a thicker than normal blank. In France, whence the term originates, the Kings seem to have issued them as presentation pieces from the 12th century onwards. In Britain medieval and Tudor examples are known, and their issue has now been reintroduced by the Royal Mint, starting with the 20 pence peidfort of 1982.

plain (on silver coins) — no provenance marks in angles between shields on reverse.

plain 4 — with upper serif only to horizontal bar of 4 (see crosslet 4).

pln edge prf — plain edge proof.

plume(s) — symbol denoting Welsh mines as source of metal.

proof, prf — coin specially struck from highly polished dies. Usually has a mirror-like surface.

prov, provenance — a provenance mark on a coin (e.g. rose, plume, elephant) indicates the supplier of the bullion from which the coin was struck.

PT — plain trident.

raised — in relief, not incuse.

RB — round beads in border.

rev — reverse, 'tail' side of coin.

r — right.

r & p — roses and plumes.

Roses and plumes provenance marks

rose — symbol denoting west of England mines as source of metal.

RRITANNIAR — lettering error.

rsd — raised.

S (on gold coins) — minted at Sydney (Australia).

SA (on gold coins) — minted at Pretoria (South Africa).

Scottish shilling 1953-66

Scot — Scottish shilling. Lion seated on crown, holding sword and sceptre (1937-51); lion rampant, on shield (1953-66).

SS C — South Sea Company (source of metal).

1723 shilling bearing the South Sea Company's initials

SEC — SECUNDO, regnal year (on edge).

sh — shield(s).

sm — small.

'spade' — refers to spadelike shape of shield on George III gold coins.

'Spade' guinea, reverse

TB — toothed beads in border.

TER — TERTIO, regnal year (on edge).

trnctn, truncation — base of head or bust where the neck or shoulders terminate.

Unc — Uncirculated condition.

var — variety.

VF — Very Fine condition.

VIGO — struck from bullion captured in Vigo Bay.

VIP — 'very important person'. The so-called VIP crowns were the true proofs for the years of issue. Probably most of the limited number struck would have been presented to high ranking officials.

W.C.C. — Welsh Copper Co (supplier of metal).

wire type — figure of value in thin wire-like script.

W.W. — initials of William Wyon, engraver.

xxri — lettering error.

y, Y (on William III coins) — minted at York.

YH — Young Head.

Victoria Young Head Maundy fourpence

Coin Grading

IT IS MOST important that newcomers to collecting should get to know the various grades of condition before attempting to buy or sell coins.

The system of grading most commonly used in Britain recognises the following main classes in descending order of quality: Brilliant Uncirculated (B.Unc, BU), Uncirculated (Unc), Extremely Fine (EF), Very Fine (VF), Fine (F), Fair, Poor.

It is not surprising that beginners get confused at their first encounter with these grades. The word 'Fine' implies a coin of high quality, yet this grade turns out to be very near the bottom of the scale and is in fact about the lowest grade acceptable to most collectors of modern coinage in Britain.

American grading

It is not really necessary to go into the details of American grading here, since it is only on a very few occasions that a British collector will order the coins he wants directly from an American dealer. However, across the Atlantic their grading system is quite different from ours, and whilst it purports to be a lot more accurate, it is actually much more prone, in our opinion, to be abused, and we prefer the English dealers' more conservative methods of grading. American dealers use many more terms than we do, ranging from Mint State to About Good. The latter could be described as 'very heavily worn, with portions of lettering, date and legend worn smooth. The date may be partly legible'. In England we would simply say 'Poor'.

Numerical method

The other area which British collectors will find difficult to evaluate is the American numerical method of describing coins as, for example, MS 70, MS 65. The MS simply stands for Mint State and an MS 65 would be described as 'an above average Uncirculated coin which may be brilliant or lightly toned but has some surface marks'. The MS system seemed to be acceptable at first but there now appear to be two schools of thought in America and you will quite frequently see coins graded in the more traditional manner as well as the MS style in sale catalogues. Fortunately American grades have not come into use in this country, although dealers have followed the American manner of embellishing coin descriptions to make them more desirable, which is understandable and in many ways can be an improvement on the old method of saying simply that the coin is 'Fine', which, of course, might not do justice to it.

Full mint lustre

There are two schools of thought on the use of the terms Brilliant Uncirculated and Uncirculated. The former is often considered to be the most useful and descriptive term for coins of copper, bronze, nickel-brass or other base metals, which display what is known as 'full mint lustre'. When this term is being used it is often necessary in the same context to employ the grade Uncirculated to describe coins which have never been in circulation but have lost the original lustre of a newly minted coin. However, some dealers and collectors tend to classify as Uncirculated all coins which have not circulated, whether they are brilliant or toned, and do not use the term Brilliant Uncirculated.

Fleur de coin

Sometimes FDC (fleur de coin) is used to define top grade coins, but this really only applies to pieces in perfect mint state, having no flaws or surface scratches. With modern methods of minting, slight damage to the surface is inevitable, except in the case of proofs, and therefore Brilliant Uncirculated or Uncirculated best describe the highest grade of modern coins.

The word 'proof' should not be used to denote a coin's condition. Proofs are pieces struck on specially prepared blanks from highly polished dies and usually have a mirror-like finish.

Opinions differ

In all this matter of condition it might be said that the grade 'is in the eye of the beholder', and there are always likely to be differences of opinion as to the exact grade of a coin. Some collectors and dealers have tried to make the existing scale of definitions more exact by adding letters such as N (Nearly), G (Good, meaning slightly better than the grade to which the letter is added), A (About or Almost) and so on. To be still more accurate, in cases where a coin wears more on one side than the other, two grades are shown, the first for the obverse, the second for the reverse thus: GVF/EF.

Additional description

Any major faults not apparent from the use of a particular grade are often described separately. These include dents and noticeable scratches, discoloration, areas of corrosion, edge knocks, holes on otherwise good quality pieces, and the like.

Middle range of grades

One should always look for wear on the highest points of the design, of course, but these vary from coin to coin. To present a comprehensive guide to exact grading one would have to illustrate every grade of every coin type in a given series, on the lines of the famous Guide to the Grading of United States Coins, by Brown and Dunn. This is a complete book in itself (over 200 pages) and obviously such a mammoth task could not be attempted in the space available here. Therefore, on the following page we present representative examples from three different periods in the British series, to illustrate the 'middle' range of coin conditions.

Still in mint state

We have already dealt with the grades BU and Unc; they both describe coins which are still in the state in which they left the Mint, and which have never passed into general circulation. They are likely to show minor scratches and edge knocks due to the mass handling processes of modern minting.

Fair and Poor

At the other end of the scale we have Fair, a grade that is applied to very worn coins which still have the main parts of the design distinguishable, and Poor which denotes a grade in which the design and rim are worn almost flat and few details are discernible.

Here we show (enlarged) examples of the grades EF, VF and F. On the left are hammered long cross pennies of Aethelred II; in the centre, from the later hammered series, are groats of Henry VIII; on the right are shillings of William IV.

Extremely Fine. This describes coins which have been put into circulation, but have received only the minimum of damage since. There may be a few slight marks or minute scratches in the field (flat area around the main design), but otherwise the coin should show very little sign of having been in circulation.

Very Fine. Coins in this condition show some amount of wear on the raised surfaces, but all other detail is still very clear. Here, all three coins have had a little wear as can be seen in the details of the hair and face. However, they are still in attractive condition from the collector's viewpoint.

Fine. In this grade coins show noticeable wear on the raised parts of the design; most other details should still be clear. The penny and the groat show a lot of wear over the whole surface. On the shilling the hair above the ear has worn flat.

Extremely Fine (EF)

Very Fine (VF)

Fine (F)

Keeping your Coins

ONCE you have started to collect coins make sure you know how to look after them properly.

Storage

Careful thought should be given to the storing of coins, for a collection which is carelessly or inadequately housed can suffer irreparable damage. Corrosion depends essentially on the presence of water vapour, and therefore coins should not be stored in damp attics or spare bedrooms, but where possible in evenly heated warm rooms. We should also point out here that one must be very careful only to pick up coins by the edges, for sweaty fingerprints contain corrosive salt. The following are suitable methods of storage.

Wooden cabinets

A collection carefully laid out in a wood cabinet is seen at its most impressive. Unfortunately, though, the modern wooden cabinets which are custom-built especially for coins are not cheap. Their main advantages are the choice of tray and hole sizes, and the fact that because the manufacturer is often himself a collector, he takes care to use only well matured woods, which have no adverse reactions on coins. Among the makers of wood cabinets are H. S. Swann, of Newcastle (01661 853129) and the Stamp and Coin Shop of St Leonards, East Sussex.

There is also a newcomer to this list: Roger Collins of North London (Tel: 0181 428 2609).

If one cannot afford a new cabinet, then a second-hand version may be the answer. These can sometimes be purchased at coin auctions, or from dealers, and can be very good value. However, it is not always easy to find one with the tray hole sizes to suit your coins.

Do-it-yourself cabinet makers should also be careful not to use new wood, which will contain corrosive moisture. In this case the best method would be to use wood from an old piece of furniture.

Albums, plastic cases and carrying cases

There are many of these on the market, and some of them are both handsome and inexpensive. There are also very attractive Italian and German-made attaché-type carrying cases for collectors, with velvet lining and different sizes of trays, and so on. These can be obtained from a number of dealers, but Collectors Gallery, 6-7 Castle Gates, Shrewsbury SY1 2AE (Tel: 01743 272140) makes a speciality of them. We would also recommend the coin album, which claims to prevent oxidization. The coins are contained in cards with crystal clear film windows enabling the collector to see both sides of the coins. The cards then slide into pages in an album, and might be a convenient method of storage, especially for the new collector. Coins International of 1-2 Melbourne Street,

A beautiful, new hand-made cabinet in the traditional style by Roger Collins

Leeds LS2 7PS (01532 434230) also offer a large range of albums, envelopes, plastic boxes and capsules, etc. Lindner Publications Ltd, 26 Queen Street, Cubbington, Leamington Spa CV32 7NA supply very useful coin and collecting boxes as well as albums. In central London, probably the best place to visit is Vera Trinder, 38 Bedford Street, WC1 (0171 836 2365/6) who does appear to keep a very good stock.

Envelopes
Plastic envelopes, being transparent, are very useful for exhibition, but we never recommend them for long-term storage purposes. They tend to make the coins 'sweat', which with copper and bronze in particular can lead to corrosion.

Manilla envelopes are much more suitable, since the paper is dry, unlike ordinary paper, and consequently they are ideal for the storage of coins. Most collectors use them in conjuction with a cardboad box, which makes for simple unobtrusive storage. This is the most inexpensive method of storing coins.

Still the best article we have seen on the storage of coins and medals, which deals with all the materials which are used, was by Mr L.R. Green, who is a Higher Conservation Officer at the Department of Coins and Medals at the British Museum. This appeared in the May 1991 issue of Spink's *Numismatic Circular*.

Magnifiers
New collectors will need to have a good magnifying glass to examine coins, and these can be obtained from W.H. Smith or most other stationers; many opticians also offer very good magnifying glasses.

Cleaning coins
In the course of each week dealers examine many coins which some poor unfortunates have unwittingly totally ruined by cleaning. They are, therefore, usually the best people to ask about the subject. One dealer tells of a bright-eyed expectant gentleman who offered his late father's very useful collection of copper coins, which he proudly said he had 'brightened up' the previous day, so as to be certain of a good offer! The dealer did not enjoy his customer's sad disappointment when he found himself unable to make any offer, but then the coins had been cleaned with harsh metal polish and looked like soldiers' buttons.

We always advise people never to clean coins unless they are very dirty or corroded. Also by 'dirt' we do not mean oxide which, on silver coins, can give a pleasing bluish tone favoured by many collectors. The following simple instructions may be of some help, but do not, of course, apply to extremely corroded coins which have been found in the ground, for if important they are the province of a museum conservationist.

Gold coins
Gold should cause collectors few problems, since it is subject to corrosion only in extreme conditions. For example, a gold coin recovered from a long spell in the sea might have a dull, rusty appearance. However, in the normal course of events a little bath in methylated spirits will improve a dirty coin. A word of warning — gold coins should not be rubbed in any way.

Silver coins
Silver will discolour easily, and is particularly susceptible to damp or chemicals in the atmosphere. A gentle brushing with a soft non-nylon bristle brush will clear loose surface dirt, but if the dirt is deep and greasy, a dip in ammonia and careful drying on cotton wool should do the trick. We should once again stress that there is no need to clean a coin which simply has a darkish tone.

Copper and bronze coins
There is no safe method of cleaning copper or bronze coins without actually harming them, and we would only recommend the use of a non-nylon, pure bristle brush to deal with dirt. There is no way of curing the ailments peculiar to these metals, namely verdigris (green spots) or bronze disease (blackish spots) permanently, and we would advise collectors not to buy pieces in such condition, unless they are very inexpensive.

How to Collect Coins

A FEW words of advice for those who have recently discovered coin collecting.

How much is it worth?

There was a time when newcomers to coin collecting would ask the question 'What is it?'. Nowadays certainly the most common question dealers hear is 'What is it worth?'. It is a sign of the times that history takes second place to value. The object of COINS MARKET VALUES is to try to place a value on all the coins produced in what is known geographically as the British Isles, in other words England, Wales, Scotland and Ireland, and the Channel Islands, as well as the Anglo-Gallic series.

This is a difficult task because many coins do not turn up in auctions or lists every year even though they are not really rare. However, we make a stab at a figure so that you the collector can at least have an idea of what you will have to pay.

How to sell your coins

Auction

There has never been a time in these islands when the potential seller of coins has had more choice. In London alone we have, in alphabetical order, Baldwins, Bonhams, Dix and Webb, Glendinings, Sothebys and Spink; and there are smaller companies up and down the country, while in Ireland there is the emergence of Ian Whyte, until now better known for stamps.

The best approach for the seller is first of all to compare all their catalogues and if possible attend the auctions so that you can see how well they are conducted. Talk it over with their experts, for you may have special cataloguing requirements and you could find that one of the firms might look after them better than the others.

An obvious coin, like say an 1887 £5, requires little expertise and will probably sell at a certain price in almost any auction. However, if you require expert cataloguing of countermarked coin or early medieval, then you need to know what the company is capable of before you discuss a rate for the job.

You should remember though that while it is not complicated to sell by auction you may have to wait at least three or four months from the time you consign the coins to the auctioneers before you receive any money. There are times when auctions manage to achieve very high prices, and other times when, for some inexplicable reason, they fail to reach even a modest reserve. **You should also bear in mind that the best deal in the long term is not always the lowest commission rate.** Finally, auctioneers will usually charge you at least 10 per cent of the knockdown price, and you should bear in mind that some buyers may also be inhibited from paying a top price by the buyer's premium, also of 10 per cent. Some firms are now charging 15%.

Dealers

The function of a dealer is to have a stock of coins for sale at marked prices. However, they will naturally only wish to buy according to the ebb and flow of their stocks. It is also true to say that dealers infinitely prefer fresh material, and if you strike at the right time it is possible that you could achieve a better price than by waiting for auction, since of course you will receive the money immediately. Generally speaking both dealers and auctioneers will not make any charge for a verbal valuation, but you should allow for the dealer to be making a profit of at least 20 per cent.

Bullion coins

Relating to Krugerrands, sovereigns, and so on, most newspapers carry the price of gold, which is fixed twice daily by a group of leading banks. Anyone can buy sovereigns, and Krugerrands and other bullion coins, and it is better this year than last now that there is no VAT on top. Normally when you sell the bullion coin you expect the coin dealer to make a few pounds profit on each coin, but don't expect a good price for a mounted coin attached to grandfather's watch chain, which will not be worth anything like the same price as an undamaged item.

How to collect coins

You should obviously purchase your coins only from a reputable dealer. How do you decide on a reputable dealer? You can be sure of some protection if you choose one who is a member of the British Numismatic Trade Association or the International Association of Professional Numismatists. Membership lists of these organisations can be obtained from the respective secretaries: Mrs Carol Carter, PO Box 474A, Thames Ditton, Surrey KT7 0WJ (tel: 0181 398 4290; fax: 0181 398 4291) and J-P. Divo (IAPN), Lowenstrasse 55, 8001 Zurich (fax: 00 41 1 225 40 99). However, many dealers are not members of either organisation, and it does not mean that they are not honest or professional. The best approach is simply to find one who will unconditionally guarantee that the coins you buy from him are genuine and accurately graded.

As a general rule you should only buy coins in the best condition available, and on this subject you will at first have to rely on the judgement of the dealer you choose. However, remember it will not always be possible to find pieces in Extremely Fine condition, for example, and it can sometimes be worth buying coins which are not quite Very Fine. In the case of great rarities, of course, you might well have to make do with a coin that is only Fine, or even Poor. If there are only six known specimens of a particular piece, and four are in museums, it seems pointless to wait 20 years for another one to be found in the ground. Over the last few years condition has become too important in many ways, and has driven away collectors, because obviously you cannot buy coins only in top condition, since in certain series that would rule out at least 50 per cent of the available specimens. It depends on the type of coin, the reign and so on, so be realistic.

It is worth taking out subscriptions with auction houses so that you can receive copies of all their catalogues, because this is an excellent way to keep up with prices as well as the collections that are being offered.

However, one should not overlook the fact that a number of dealers produce price lists, which in many ways are most useful to the collector, because he can choose coins at his leisure by mail order, and can more easily work out what he can afford to buy than when in the hot-house atmosphere of the auction room. The most famous list is Spink's *Numismatic Circular* first published in 1892, and still going strong with ten issues a year. It is much more than a price list being an important forum for numismatic debate and the reporting of new finds, etc (annual subscription £15).

There are also many expert dealers who produce excellent lists, many of them advertise in this publication and obviously we cannot mention them all here, but a good cross section of those who list domestic coins, and not listed in any order of preference, is as follows:

Lloyd Bennett, PO Box 2, Monmouth, Gwent NP5 3YE. Hammered, Milled, Tokens.
B.J. Dawson, 52 St Helens Road, Bolton, Lancs BL3 3NH. Hammered, Milled, Tokens, Medals.
Dolphin Coins, 2c Englands Lane, Hampstead, London NW3 4TG. All British.
Patrick Finn, PO Box 26, Kendal, Cumbria LA9 7AB. Hammered English, Irish, Scottish.
Format, 18/19 Bennetts Hill, Birmingham B2 5QJ. All British.
Grantham Coins, PO Box 60, Grantham, Lincs. Milled, good on Maundy.
K.B. Coins, 50 Lingfield Road, Martins Wood, Stevenage, Herts SG1 5SL. Hammered and Milled.
C.J. Martin, 85 The Vale, Southgate, London N14 6AT. Celtic and Hammered.
Peter Morris, PO Box 223, Bromley, Kent BR1 4EQ. Hammered, Milled, Tokens.
S.R. Porter, 18 Trinity Road, Headington

Quarry, Oxford OX3 8LQ. Milled and Hammered.

Chris Rudd, PO Box 222, Aylsham, Norfolk NR11 6TY. The only specialist dealer in Celtic Coins.

Seaby Coins, 14 Old Bond Street, London W1X 4JL. Hammered, some Milled.

Simmons & Simmons, PO Box 104, Leytonstone, London E11 1ND.

Also, don't forget there are specialist dealers who do not produce lists, for example, Chelsea Coins (Dimitri Loulakakis, 0181 879 5501) who is the man for maundy coins.

Societies

You should consider joining your local numismatic society, there being quite a number of these throughout the country. To find if there is one near you, contact the President of the British Association of Numismatic Societies, Miss M. A. Archibald, Department of Coins and Medals, British Museum, Great Russell Street, London WC1. The BANS organises annual congresses and seminars, and it is a good idea for the serious collector to consider attending one of these. Details are usually well publicised in the numismatic press.

Those collectors who wish to go a little further can apply for membership of the British Numismatic Society, and for their annual membership fee they will receive a copy of the *British Numismatic Journal* which incorporates details of current research and many important articles, as well as book reviews. Another useful facet of membership of this Society is that you can borrow books from its library in the Warburg Institute. Londoners might like to consider joining the London Numismatic Society, which is the best society after the Royal and the British, and is always looking for new members. Newcomers will be sure of a very friendly reception. The secretary is Mrs Stella Greenall, c/o P. Rueff, 2 King's Bench Walk, The Temple, London EC4Y 7DE.

Museums and where to see Coins

The British Museum has the greatest collection of domestic coins and a visit there, by appointment, is a must for the serious student. By making an appointment the student is able to look at specific sections, under supervision. For example, a sensible request would be to look at, say, Victorian bronze pennies. There are so many of these that it could take a few hours. As far as exhibitions are concerned, at the present time there is a very good one in the Greek and Roman Life Room but no detailed exhibition of British coins.

The National Museum of Antiquities in Edinburgh under Donal Bateson is well worth a visit to see some of the coins from the famous Hunter collection, while the Ashmolean Museum in Oxford has a particularly good staff and is very friendly and accessible. The Fitzwilliam in Cambridge now houses both the famous Grierson collection and the legendary collection of British coins formed by the late Christopher Blunt. It is under the curatorship of Mark Blackburn, one of the most respected younger numismatists in the country.

There is an attractive coin and medal gallery at the Cathay Park headquarters of the National Museum of Wales run by the enthusiastic Edward Besley. Greek, Roman, Celtic and a chronological view of the coinage of England and Wales from the Iron Age to the present day are beautifully presented. This Museum is open every day except Monday.

The Ulster Museum in Belfast has some very interesting display techniques and certainly makes the most of a relatively small collection. Most of this was done under the directorship of Bill Seaby in the 1970s, but the present coin specialist, Robert Heslop, will always be very helpful. The National Museum of Ireland in Dublin has a very important collection but is presently being rehoused. The man in charge there, Michael Kenny, is particularly helpful, and hopefully will have more time for coins when his busy move is completed.

There are many other museums up and down the country which have excellent collections of early British coins. The following are well worth a visit:

City Museum and Art Gallery, Chamberlain Square, Birmingham B3 3DH (0120 235 2834). Especially good for coins produced in Birmingham.

Blackburn Museum, Museum Street, Blackburn, Lancs (01254 867170). Has a good reputation for numismatics.

City Museum, Queen's Road, Bristol BS8 1RL (01179 223571). Especially good on coins of the Bristol mint.

Royal Albert Memorial Museum, Queen Street, Exeter EX4 3RX (01392 265858). Has a very good collection of Exeter mint coins.

Manx Museum, Douglas, Isle of Man (01624 675522). Particularly excellent for students of Viking and Hiberno-Norse.

City Museum, Municipal Buildings, The Headrow, Leeds, W Yorkshire (01132 478279). An excellent all round collection.

Manchester Museum, The University, Manchester M13 (0161 2752634). Another excellent all round collection.

Reading Museum and Art Gallery, Blagrave Street, Reading, Berks (01735 399809). Good medieval and interesting local finds.

The Yorkshire Museum, Museum Gardens, York YO1 2DR (01904 629745). Good for medieval and later English.

Many of our museums have cooperated with the British Academy to produce a wonderful series of books under the heading of Sylloge of coins of the British Isles which now runs to over 40 volumes. Some of these volumes refer to coins held in Museums overseas, but we list here the ones which deal with coins in these islands, and this will give students a better idea of some of the material they have for study.

1   Fitzwilliam Museum, Cambridge. Ancient British and Anglo-Saxon Coins, by P. Grierson
2   Hunterian Museum, Glasgow. Anglo-Saxon Coins, by A.S. Robertson
5   Grosvenor Museum, Chester. Coins with the Chester Mint-Signature, by E.J.E. Pirie
6   National Museum of Antiquities of Scotland, Edinburgh. Anglo-Saxon Coins, by R.B.K. Stevenson

Coin Fairs

Whilst it is always important to visit museums to see coins, it is worth remembering that there is often a fine array on show at coin fairs around the country, and most dealers do not mind showing coins to would-be collectors, even if they cannot buy them on the spot.

The BNTA have been very successful with the COINEX shows, and the annual event at the Marriott Hotel should not be missed (October 1996). Likewise COINEX WALES held in Cardiff each Spring (for further details contact BNTA Secretary 0181 398 4290).

Howard and Frances Simmons are the popular organisers of the Cumberland Coin shows since the late 1960s (for details ring 0181 989 8097).

The Croydon team of Davidson/Monk organise the monthly shows at the Great Western, Paddington (ring 0181 656 4583).

David Fletcher organises the monthly Midland Coin & Stamp Fair, second Sunday every month (enquiries 01203 716160).

Finally for details of the successful Irish coin shows in Dublin ring Peter Sheen (003531 496 4390); and for the annual show in conjunction with the Irish Numismatic Society ring Ian Whyte (003531 874 6161).

Forgeries

MOST collectors know that there have been forgeries since the earliest days of coin production, so it is only to be expected that some new forgeries appear on the scene every year. It seems that there is always someone willing to deceive the collector and the dealer. However, nowadays very few forgers end up making much money. As a result of the actions of the British Numismatic Trade Association, the trade is much more tightly knit than ever before, and anxious to stamp out new forgeries before they have a chance to become a serious menace.

They were last a matter of serious concern in the late 1960s and early 1970s, when an enormous number of 1887 £5 pieces and United States $20 manufactured in Beirut came on to the market. Also in the early 1970s the group of Dennington forgeries could have made a serious impact on the English hammered gold market, but for lucky early detection. (Unfortunately we have noticed a number of these are still in circulation, and so we will deal with them later in this article.)

In the late 1970s a crop of forgeries of Ancient British coins came to light causing a panic in academic and trade circles. This caused a lack of confidence in the trade and it has taken a number of years for everyone to feel happy that there was no further problem. The BNTA firmly pursues any mention of forgeries and one hopes that a new spate of copies of Anglo-Saxon coins from the West Country are not allowed to develop. They are being sold as replicas, but they are still deceptive in the wrong hands. The IAPN has produced a list of these in 1995/6 Vol. 20 No. 2.

The worrying forgeries

We mentioned earlier the 'Dennington' forgeries. It is now many years since the trial of Anthony Dennington at the Central Criminal Court, where he was found guilty on six charges of 'causing persons to pay money by falsely pretend- ing that they were buying genuine antique coins' *The Times,* July 10, 1969). There is a small number of these pieces still circulating in the trade, and since they have deceived some collectors and dealers, we thought we should record them more fully here. The following is a list of the pieces which appeared in the IBSCC Bulletin in August 1976.

1   Henry III gold penny
2   Edward III Treaty period noble
3   Another, with saltire before King's name
4   Henry IV heavy coinage noble
5   Henry V noble, Class C (mullet at King's sword arm)
6   Henry V/VI mule noble
7   Henry VI noble, annulet issue, London
8   Edward IV ryal, Norwich
9   Another, York
10 Elizabeth I Angel

Dennington forgeries: Edward III noble (top) and Mary Fine sovereign

11 Mary Fine Sovereign 1553
12 James I unite, mintmark mullet
13 James I rose ryal, 3rd coinage, mint mark lis
14 James I 3rd coinage laurel
15 Commonwealth unite 1651
16 Commonwealth half unite 1651
17 Charles II touch piece

One can only reiterate that these copies are generally very good and you must beware of them. The following points may be useful.

1   The coins are usually slightly 'shiny' in appearance, and the edges are not good, since they have been filed down and polished.

2   They are usually very 'hard' to touch, whereas there is a certain amount of 'spring' in the genuine articles.

3   They usually feel slightly thick, but not always, not quite like an electro-type but certainly thicker than normal.

4   Although the Mary Fine sovereign reproduction is heavy, at 16.1986 gr, these pieces are usually lighter in weight than the originals.

As far as forgeries of modern coins are concerned, the most worrying aspect has been the enormous increase in well produced forgeries in the last 25 years.

They are so well produced that it is often impossible for the naked eye to detect the difference, and it has therefore become the job of the scientist and metallurgist. Many of these pieces have deceived dealers and collectors, although they do not seem to have caused too great a crisis of confidence. This increase in the number of modern counterfeits has been due to the enormous rise in coin values since the early 1960s.

It is well known that the vast majority of these modern forgeries has emanated from the Middle East, as we have suggested earlier, where it is *not* illegal to produce counterfeits of other countries' coins. It has proved to be very good business for a lot of these small forgers in Beirut, and one can only rely on the alertness of the coin trade so that reports are circulated quickly whenever a new forgery is spotted.

Unfortunately, the main problem is still that the forger has every encouragement to continue production of copies, when one thinks of the profit involved. At the time of writing, it only takes about £290 worth of gold to make an 1887-dated five pound piece of correct composition, valued at around £650. We cannot, therefore, be complacent.

There is not enough space here to tell you in detail what to look for, and anyway detecting forgeries requires specialist knowledge, so a list of faults would not help. If you turn to the catalogue section of COINS MARKET VALUES you will find that as far as British coins are concerned we have placed **(F)** beside a number of coins which we know have been counterfeited, and which frequently turn up. However, you should watch out for sovereigns, in particular, of which there are forgeries of every date from 1900 to 1932 and even recent dates such as 1957 and 1976.

A list follows of the pieces you should be particularly careful about, especially if you notice that they are being offered below the normal catalogue value. Most modern forgeries of, say, Gothic crowns, seem to be offered at prices which are 10 per cent or 20 per cent below the current market price. The moral is, do not automatically think you have a bargain if the price is low — it could be a forgery!

Modern cast copies of Anglo-Saxon pennies: Ceolwulf 1st above, and Ceonwulf below

1738, 1739 two guineas
1793, 1798 guineas (there could
    also be other dates)
1820 pattern two pounds
1839 five pounds (in particular the
    plain edge variety)
1887 five pounds
1887 two pounds (there seem to be
    many forgeries of these)
1893 five pounds, two pounds
1902 five pounds, two pounds
1911 five pounds, two pounds
1817, 1819, 1822, 1825, 1827,
    1887, 1889, 1892, 1892M,
    1908C, 1913C sovereigns;
    also every date from 1900 to
    1932 inclusive, plus 1957,
    1959, 1963, 1966, 1967,
    1974, 1976
1847 Gothic crowns
1905 halfcrowns

Other safeguards against forgery

(a) The best method of protection against purchasing forgeries is to buy your coins from a reputable dealer who is a member of the British Numismatic Trade Association or the International Association of Professional Numismatists, or one who will unconditionally guarantee that all his coins are genuine.

(b) Legal tender coins, which include five and two pound pieces, sovereigns, half sovereigns and crowns, are protected by the Forgery and Counterfeiting Act, and it is the responsibility of the police to prosecute in cases where this Act has been contravened.

(c) If your dealer is unhelpful over a non legal tender item which you have purchased and which you think has been falsely described, you can take legal action under the Trades Description Act 1968. However, we should warn you that it can be a tedious and long-winded business, but if you want to proceed in this you should contact your local Trading Standards Office or Consumer Protection department.

THE INAFB

The best known professional opponent of the forger in the British Isles is E.G.V. Newman, formerly of the Royal Mint. He has been providing an excellent service to traders and collectors for many years now, and is expert, especially on modern machine-made coins, and in particular gold £5, £2, sovereigns and so on. Mr Newman's organisation, the INAFB (International Numismatic Anti-Forgery Bureau) is a completely independent body.

Members of the public may send coins to MNC Ltd, PO Box 52, Farnham, Surrey GU10 4JR.

The INAFB charges are, per item:

Insured value of coin	Charge
Up to £100	£3
£101-£1,000	3% of insured value
£1,001-£2,500	£35
£2,501-£5,000	£40
£5,001-£10,000	£45
Over £10,000	£50

A charge will be made for return registered postage, packing and intransit insurance from £5 upwards according to destination.

Note that no legal responsibility in respect of any claim made as a result of this opinion will be accepted by the Director or the INAFB.

A 'Behra' counterfeit of the 1950s. The last of a series bearing the dates 1902 to 1920, where the original pattern piece was a genuine South African sovereign of unknown date but post 1924. An attempt was made to remove the SA mint mark on the tool used to prepare the dies but traces still remained and were transferred to all the dies

The different types of forgery

There are many different forgeries, but essentially they can be divided into two main groups. First of all there are contemporary forgeries intended to be used as face-value money (as in the cases, some years ago, of the counterfeit 50p pieces, which even worked in slot machines), and secondly forgeries intended to deceive collectors.

Contemporary forgeries, those pieces struck in imitation of currency coins, are obviously not a serious problem to numismatists. The recent ones cause more trouble to bank clerks, anyway, and are not of sufficiently good standard to deceive numismatic experts. In general, those produced in the Middle Ages were base (which was how the forger made a profit), consisting wholly of base metal or occasionally having a thin coating of the proper metal on the outside. Sometimes they were struck, but more often they were cast. Whatever the problems they caused at the time of issue, they are now often as interesting as the regular coins of the period.

However, one can be less light-hearted about copies which are made to deceive collectors. The following five methods of production have been used.

1. Electrotyping. These copies would not normally deceive an expert.

2. Casting. Old casts are easily recognisable, having marks made by air bubbles on the surface, and showing a generally 'fuzzy' effect. Much more of a problem are the modern cast copies, produced by sophisticated 'pressure-casting', which can be extremely difficult for all but the most expert to distinguish from the originals (more of this later).

3. The fabrication of false dies. With hammered coins counterfeits are not difficult for an expert to detect. However, the sophisticated die production techniques used in Beirut have resulted in the worrying features of modern gold and silver coins described later.

4. The use of genuine dies put to some illegal use such as restriking (a mintmaster in West Germany was convicted in 1975 of that very issue).

5. Alteration of a genuine coin. (Ask your dealer how many George V pennies he has seen with the date altered to 1933 — it does happen!)

British Coin Prices

ANCIENT BRITISH

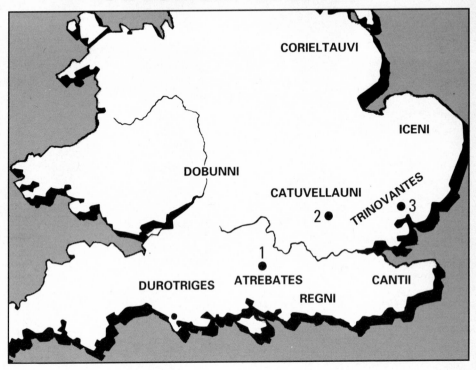

CORIELTAUVI

ICENI

DOBUNNI

CATUVELLAUNI

TRINOVANTES

2●

●3

1
●

DUROTRIGES   ATREBATES

CANTII

REGNI

The distribution of the tribes in Britain
based on the map in 'The Coinage of
Ancient Britain', by R. P. Mack, published
by Spink and Son Ltd and B. A. Seaby Ltd.

Key to towns:
1. Calleva Atrebatum (Silchester)
2. Verulamium (St Albans)
3. Camulodunum (Colchester)

It is always difficult to produce a priced catalogue of coins, but none is more difficult
than the early British series. The market has developed considerably since the publication
of R. D. Van Arsdell's *Celtic Coinage of Britain*, which is an essential book for collectors
(584 pages, 54 plates and many other illustrations, maps and diagrams).

A word of caution, though; quite a number of forgeries exist, some of relatively
recent production, and unfortunately also numerous items from undeclared hoards are
on the market, which makes it essential to buy from a reputable dealer.

We are very grateful for the help of Robert Van Arsdell since he produced the
synopsis of the material which we have used. We have kept this very basic, and
simply linked it up for easy reference with *The Coinage of Ancient Britain* by R. P.
Mack, third edition, London 1975 (now out of print), and with Seaby's *Standard
Catalogue* Part 1. In the following lists Mack types are indicated by 'M' and Seaby
types by 'S'. The V numbers relate to the Van Arsdell catalogue. The existence of
forgeries is indicated by **(F)**.

Gold staters without legends

AMBIANI

	F	VF
Large flan type M1, 3, S1, V10, 12 ...	**£500**	**£1800**

Ambiani large flan type

	F	VF
Defaced die type M5, 7, S3, V30, 33...	**£400**	**£1000**
Abstract type M26, 30, S5, V44, 46 ...	**£260**	**£600**
Gallic War type M27, a, S7, V50, 52 **(F)**	**£130**	**£260**

Gallic War gold stater

SUESSIONES

Abstract type M34a, S8, V85	**£300**	**£700**

VE MONOGRAM

M82, a, b, S9, V87 **(F)**	**£275**	**£600**

WESTERHAM

M28, 29, S19, V200, 202	**£250**	**£475**

CHUTE

M32, S20, V1205 **(F)**	**£140**	**£240**

CLACTON

Type I M47, S24, V1458	**£260**	**£575**
Type II M46, a, S25, V30, 1455	**£250**	**£520**

CORIELTAUVI

Type I M50-51a, S26, V800...	**£200**	**£450**
Type II M52-57, S27, V804...	**£275**	**£550**

Norfolk Wolf star VA610-3

NORFOLK

Wolf type M49, a, b, S28, V610 ...	**£200**	**£450**

	F	VF

CORIELTAUVI

South Ferriby type, M449-450a, S.30, V.811	**£180**	**£400**

Coritani (South Ferriby)

WHADDON CHASE

M133-138, V1470-1478 **(F)**	**£140**	**£320**
Middle, Late Whaddon Chase V1485-1509	**£220**	**£500**

Whaddon Chase

WONERSH

M147, 148, S37, V1522	**£375**	**£650**

WEALD

M84, 292, S35, V144, 150	**£350**	**£800**

ICENI

Type I M397-399, 403b, S38, V620 ...	**£250**	**£500**
Type II M401, 2, 3, 3a, 3c, S39, V626 ...	**£300**	**£600**

Iceni gold stater

ATREBATIC

M58-61, S41-2, V210-216	**£250**	**£450**

Atrebatic stater

SAVERNAKE FOREST

M62, S42, V1526	**£150**	**£350**

DOBUNNIC

M374, S43, V1005	**£300**	**£700**

Gold quarter staters without legends

	F	VF
AMBIANI		
Large flan type M2, 4, S2, V15, 20 ...	£250	£650
Defaced die type M6, 8, S4, V35, 37 ...	£200	£450
GEOMETRIC		
M37, 39, 41, 41A, 42, S6, V65, 146, 69, 67	£75	£190
SUSSEX		
M40, 43-45, S49, V143, 1225-1229 ...	£70	£160
VE MONOGRAM		
M83, S10, V87 **(F)**	£160	£350

Atrebatic quarter stater, Bognor Cog Wheel

	F	VF
ATREBATIC		
M63-67, 69-75, S51, V220-256	£100	£275

Caesar's trophy, quarter stater VA145

	F	VF
KENTISH		
Caesar's Trophy type V145	£100	£200
ATREBATIC		
M63-67, 69-75, S51, V220-256	£100	£275

Gold staters with legends

	F	VF
COMMIUS		
M92, S85, V350	£800	£2000
TINCOMARUS		
M93, 93, S86, V362, 363	£600	£1500
VERICA		
Equestrian type M121, S98, V500 ...	£350	£800
Vine leaf type M125, S99, V520	£500	£950

Verica gold stater

	F	VF
EPATICCUS		
M262, S112, V575	£600	£1500

	F	VF
DUBNOVELLAUNUS		
In Kent M283, S118, V176	£400	£900
In Essex M275, S152, V1650...... ...	£450	£950
EPPILLUS		
In Kent M300-1, S127-8, V430	£600	£1500
ADDEDOMAROS		
M266, 7, S148, V1605 **(F)**	£200	£500
TASCIOVANUS		
Bucranium M149, S157, V1680 **(F)** ...	£250	£600

VOLISIOS DUMNOCOVEROS

	F	VF
Equestrian M154-7, S158, V1730-1736	£275	£500
TASCIO/RICON M184, S161, V1780...	£700	£1600
ANDOCO		
M197, S202, V1860	£500	£1100

Tasciovanus Celtic Warrior

	F	VF
CUNOBELINE		
Two horses M201, S207, V1910... ...	£700	£1500
Corn ear M203 etc, S208, V2010 **(F)**...	£240	£500

ANDOCO Stater

	F	VF
ANTED of the Dobunni		
M385-6, S260, V1062-1066 **(F)**	£450	£900
EISU		
M388, S262, V1105 **(F)**	£700	£1500
INAM		
M390, S264, V1140 **(F)**	extremely rare	
CATTI		
M391, S265, V1130 **(F)**	£450	£800
COMUX		
M392, S266, V1092 **(F)**	£650	£1500
CORIO		
M393, S267, V1035	£450	£800

	F	VF
BODVOC		
M395, S269, V1052 **(F)**	**£650**	**£1400**

Bodvoc

VEP CORF		
M459-460. S291, V940, 930 **(F)**	**£450**	**£950**

DUMNOC TIGIR SENO		
M461, S299, V972 **(F)**	**£750**	**£1500**

VOLISIOS DUMNOCOVEROS		
M463, S301, V978	**£450**	**£850**

Cunobeline Stater

Gold quarter staters with legends

TINCOMARUS	F	VF
Abstract type M95, S87, V365	**£275**	**£500**
Medusa head type M97, S89, V387 ...	**£300**	**£600**
Tablet type M101-4, S90, V387-390 ...	**£170**	**£350**

Tincommius Medusa head gold quarter stater

EPPILLUS		
CALLEVA M107, S95, V407	**£130**	**£250**

Eppillus CALLEVA type

VERICA	F	VF
Horse type M111-114, S100,		
V465-468	**£120**	**£250**

TASCIOVANUS		
Horse type M152-3, S163, V1690,		
1692	**£130**	**£275**

CUNOBELINE		
Corn ear M204, 9, S211, V2015,		
1927	**£100**	**£250**

Silver coins without legends

DUROTRIGES			
Silver stater M317, S60, V1235 **(F)**	...	**£35**	**£110**
Geometric type M319, S61, V1242	...	**£35**	**£85**
Starfish type M320, S61A, V1270	...	**£50**	**£100**

Starfish Unit

DOBUNNIC			
Face M374a, b, 5, 6, 8, S63, V1020		**£25**	**£60**
Abstract M378a-384d, S64, V1042	...	**£15**	**£45**

CORIELTAUVI			
Boar type M405a, S66, V855	... ...	**£75**	**£160**
South Ferriby M410 etc, S68, V875	...	**£50**	**£100**

Coritani, showing boar and horse

ICENI			
Boar type M407-9, S72, V655-659	...	**£35**	**£90**
Wreath type M414, 5, 440, S75, V679,			
675		**£15**	**£45**
Face type M412-413e, S74, V665	...	**£40**	**£100**

QUEEN BOUDICA			
Face type M413, 413D, V790, 792	...	**£70**	**£150**

Silver coins of Boudica (left) and Commius (right)

COMMIUS		
Head left M446b, V355, 357...	**£50**	**£125**

Silver coins with legends

EPPILLUS	F	VF
CALLEVA type M108, S96, V415... ...	**£55**	**£120**

EPATICCUS			
Eagle type M263, S113, V580	... ...	**£30**	**£95**
Victory type M263a, S114, V581	...	**£35**	**£120**

Silver unit, Epaticcus

CARATACUS	F	VF
Eagle Type M265, S117, V593 **(F)** ...	£150	£350

TASCIOVANUS
Equestrian M158, S167, V1745	£90	£250
VER type M161, S170, V1699	£90	£220

CUNOBELINE
Equestrian M216-8, S215, 6, V1951, 1953, 2047	£70	£160
Bust right M236, S221, VA2055	£100	£250

ANTED of the Dobunni
M387, S261, V1082	£80	£160

EISU
M389, S263, V1110	£90	£200

BODVOC
M396, S270, V1057 **(F)**	£130	£400

ANTED of the Iceni
M419-421, S273, V710, 711, 715 ...	£15	£30

ECEN
M424, S275, V730	£18	£35

EDNAM
M423, 425b, S277, V740, 734	£40	£80

ECE
M425a, 426, 7, 8, S278-280, V761, 764, 762, 766	£20	£40

AESU
M432, S282, V775	£70	£150

PRASUTAGUS
King of the Iceni (husband of Boudica)	£650	£1100

ESUP ASU
M4566, S289, VA924	£400	*

VEP CORF
M460b, 464, S292, V394, 950	£150	£300

DUMNOC TIGIR SENO
M462, S300, V974...	£150	£350

VOLISIOS DUMNOCOVEROS
M463a, S302, V978, 980	£150	£350

ALE SCA
M469, S285, V996...	£300	*

Bronze, base metal coins without legends

POTIN
	F	VF
Experimental type M22a, S83, V104	£60	£110

Potin coin class II

	F	VF
Class I M9-22, S83, V122-131	£20	£65
Class II M23-25, S84, V136-139 ...	£35	£95
Thurrock Types V1402-1442	£25	£50

ARMORICAN
Billon stater S12-17	£30	£75
Billon quarter stater S18	£40	£100

DUROTRIGES
Bronze stater M318, S81, V1290 ...	£25	£50
Cast type M322-370, S82, V1322-1370	£45	£90

NORTH THAMES
M273, 274, 281, S77, V1646, 1615, 1669	£45	£120

NORTH KENT
M295, 296, S80, V154...	£80	£170

Bronze coins with legends

DUBNOVELLAUNUS in Essex
	F	VF
M277, 8, S154, V1665, 1667...	£50	£140

TASCIOVANUS
Head, beard M168, 9, S179, V1707 ...	£50	£150
VERLAMIO M172, S183, V1808	£50	£150
Head, VER M177, S189, V1816	£70	£200
Boar, VER M179, S191, V1713	£80	£250
Equestrian M190, S195, V1892	£70	£200
Centaur M192, S197, V1882...	£80	£250

ANDOCO
M200, S205, V1871...	£150	£400

CUNOBELINE
Victory, TASC M221, S233, V1971 ...	£60	£150
Victory, CUN M22, a, S234, V1973 ...	£50	£100
Winged animal, M225, S237, V2081...	£60	£120

Cunobeline bronze with Centaur reverse

Head, beard, M226, 9, S238, V2131, 2085	£70	£150
Panel, sphinx, M230, S241, V1977 ...	£70	£150
Winged beast, M231, S242, V1979 ...	£70	£150
Centaur, M242, S245, V2089...	£50	£200
Sow, M243, S246, V2091	£50	£120
Warrior, M244, S247, V2093...	£40	£120
Boar, TASC, M245, S248, V1983... ...	£75	£200
Bull, TASC, M246, S249, V2095... ...	£50	£100
Metal worker, M248, S251, V2097 ...	£60	£150
Pegasus, M249, S252, V2099	£70	£150
Horse, CAMV, M250, S253, V2101 ...	£65	£150
Jupiter, horse, M251, S254, V2103 ...	£65	£200
Janus head, M252, S255, V2105... ...	£80	£250
Jupiter, lion, M253, S256, V2107... ...	£60	£150
Sphinx, fig, M260, a, S257, V2109 ...	£65	£200

ENGLISH HAMMERED
Gold from 1344 and Silver from *circa* 600

Prices in this section are approximately what collectors can expect to pay for the commonest types of the coins listed; for most other types prices will range upwards from these amounts. Precise valuations cannot be given since they vary from dealer to dealer and, in any case, have to be determined by consideration of a number of factors eg, the coin's condition (which is of prime importance in deciding its value);

For more detailed information refer to *English Hammered Coins,* Volumes 1 and 2, by J.J. North and published by Spink and Son Ltd. Any serious collector should obtain a copy of the important new volume, *The Herbert Schneider Collection of English Gold Coins 1257-1603*, published by Spink and Son, 1996.

GOLD COINS
The Plantagenet Kings

Henry III gold penny

HENRY III 1216-1272   F   VF
Gold Penny ... ...
This specimen sold for £159,500 (including buyers premium) at a Spink auction on 9 July 1996.

Edward III quarter noble

EDWARD III 1327-77   F   VF
Third coinage
Florins or Double leopard ... ...   ext. rare
Half florins or leopards   ... ...   ext. rare
Quarter florins or helms   ... ...   ext. rare
Nobles ... ...   from **£800 £2000**
Half nobles **£1200 £3500**
Quarter nobles **£300   £800**

Fourth coinage
Pre-treaty with France (i.e. before 1315) with French title
Nobles **£300   £650**
Half nobles **£200   £390**
Quarter nobles **£100   £300**
Transitional treaty period, 1361. Aquitaine title added
Nobles **£300   £650**
Half nobles **£170   £400**
Quarter nobles **£125   £275**
Treaty period 1361-9 omits FRANC
Nobles, London **£275   £550**

Nobles, Calais
(C in centre of rev.) **£290   £700**
Half nobles, London **£190   £350**
Half nobles, Calais **£275   £600**
Quarter nobles, London **£110   £250**
Quarter nobles, Calais **£150   £300**

Post-treaty period 1369-77 French title resumed
Nobles, London **£300   £650**
Nobles, Calais
(flag at stern or C in centre) **£375   £700**
Half nobles, London ... ...   ext. rare
Half nobles, Calais **£400   £900**
There are many other issues and varieties in this reign. These prices relate to the commoner pieces.

Richard II Noble of London
RICHARD II 1377-99
Nobles, London **£500   £900**
Nobles, Calais
(flag at stern) **£550 £1100**
Half nobles, London **£475 £1250**
Half nobles, Calais
(flag at stern) **£650 £1800**
Quarter nobles, London **£300   £700**
There are many different varieties and different styles of lettering.

HENRY IV 1399-1413
Heavy coinage
Nobles (120grs), London ... ...   **£3000   ***
Nobles, Calais (flag at stern) ... ...   ext. rare
Half nobles, London ... ...   ext. rare
Half nobles, Calais ... ...   ext. rare
Quarter nobles, London **£950 £2000**
Quarter nobles, Calais **£1000 £2500**

Light coinage
Nobles (108grs) **£750 £1750**
Half nobles ... ...   **£2500   ***
Quarter nobles **£450   £950**

Henry V noble

HENRY V 1413-22

	F	VF
Nobles, many varieties, from	£375	£650
Half nobles	£350	£750
Quarter nobles	£175	£350

This reign sees an increase in the use of privy marks to differentiate issues.

Henry VI noble, Annulet issue

HENRY VI 1422-61
Annulet issue (1422-27)

	F	VF
Nobles, London	£300	£600
Nobles, Calais (flag at stern)	£400	£900
Nobles, York	£450	£950
Half nobles, London	£220	£450
Half nobles, Calais	£400	£850
Half nobles, York	£400	£850
Quarter nobles, London	£120	£275
Quarter nobles, Calais	£200	£450
Quarter nobles, York	£250	£475

Rosette-mascle issue 1427-30

	F	VF
Nobles, London	£525	£1250
Nobles, Calais	£600	£1500
Half nobles, London	£750	£1500
Half nobles, Calais	£900	£1800
Quarter nobles, London	£250	£500
Quarter nobles, Calais	£350	£650

Pinecone-mascle issue 1430-4

	F	VF
Nobles, London	£600	£1250
Half nobles, London		ext. rare
Quarter noble		unique

Henry VI quarter noble, leaf-muscle

	F	VF
Leaf-mascle issue 1434-5		
Nobles	£1500	£3000
Half nobles		ext. rare
Quarter nobles	£1250	£2500
Leaf-trefoil issue 1435-8		
Nobles		ext. rare
Quarter noble		unique
Trefoil issue 1438-43		
Nobles	£1500	£3500
Leaf-pellet issue 1445-54		
Nobles	£1500	£3500

Henry VI noble, leaf-pellet

	F	VF
Cross-pellet issue 1454-60		
Nobles		unique
EDWARD IV 1st reign 1461-70		
Heavy coinage 1461-64/5		
Nobles (108grs)	£3500	*
Quarter noble		unique

Edward IV noble, heavy coinage

Light coinage 1464-70

	F	VF
Ryals or rose nobles (120grs),		
London	£300	£600
Flemish copy....	£275	£475
Ryals, Bristol (B in waves)	£400	£800
Ryals, Coventry (C in waves)	£600	£1400
Ryals, Norwich (N in waves)	£700	£1600
Ryals, York (E in waves)	£350	£800
Half ryals, London	£275	£450
Half ryals, Bristol (B in waves)	£350	£850
Half ryals, Coventry (C in waves)	£850	*
Half ryals, Norwich (N in waves) ...	£1000	*
Half ryals, York (E in waves) ...	£300	£650
Quarter ryals	£190	£400
Angels	£3500	*

HAMMERED GOLD

Edward IV angel, first reign

HENRY VI (restored) 1470-71
Angels, London	£500	£1300
Angels, Bristol (B in waves)	£800	£2000
Half angels, London	£1500	£3500
Half angels, Bristol (B in waves) ...	unique	

EDWARD IV 2nd reign 1471-83
Angels, London	£200	£480
Angels, Bristol (B in waves)	£800	£2000
Half angels, some varieties	£200	£475

EDWARD IV or V
mm halved sun and rose
Angels	£950	£2500

EDWARD V 1483
mm boar's head on obverse, halved
sun and rose on reverse.
Angels	£7000	*
Half angel	ext. rare	

RICHARD III 1483-5
Angel, reading EDWARD, with R over E by mast	unique	
Angels, as before, but *mm* boar's head	unique	
Angels, reading RICARD or RICAD ...	£700	£1500
Half angels	£3500	*

Richard III half angel

The Tudor Monarchs

Henry VII sovereign

HENRY VII 1485-1509
	F	VF
Sovereigns of 20 shillings (all ext. rare) from	£4500	£9500
Ryals	£8000	£16000
Angels, varieties, different *mm* from	£275	£475
Half angels	£200	£425

HENRY VIII 1509-47
First coinage 1509-26
Sovereigns of 20 shillings *mm* crowned portcullis only	£3000	*
Angels (6s 8d) ... ... from	£275	£600
Half angels	£200	£450

Second coinage 1526-44
Sovereigns of 22s 6d, various *mm*	£2500	£6000
Angels (7s 6d)	£275	£650
Half angels *mm* lis	£450	£950
George-nobles *mm* rose	£2500	£6000
Half-George noble	unique	
Crowns of the rose *mm* rose	ext. rare	

(Very seldom on the market – one fetched £10,000 + 10% at Sotheby's in May 1994).

Henry VIII crown of the double rose

Crowns of the double-rose		
HK (Henry and Katherine of Aragon)	£250	£500
HA (Henry and Anne Boleyn) ...	£300	£700
HI (Henry and Jane Seymour) ...	£350	£600
HR (HENRICUS REX)	£190	£450
Halfcrowns of the double-rose		
HK	£250	£650
HI	£250	£650
HR	£375	£750

Third coinage 1544-47
Sovereigns of 20s, London ... from	£1800	£5000
Sovereigns of 20s, Southwark ...	£1600	£3500
Sovereigns of 20s, Bristol	£2750	£6000
Half sovereigns, London	£295	£575
Half sovereigns, Southwark	£350	£700
Half sovereigns, Bristol	£400	£950
Angels	£250	£450
Half Angels	£250	£450
Quarter angels	£250	£475
Crowns, HENRIC 8, London	£200	£450
Crowns, Southwark	£250	£475
Crowns, Bristol	£250	£500
Halfcrowns, London	£200	£450
Halfcrowns, Southwark	£250	£500
Halfcrowns, Bristol	£275	£600

EDWARD VI 1547-53
Posthumous coinage in name of Henry VIII (1547-51)
Sovereigns, London	£2000	£4500
Sovereigns, Bristol	£2250	£5000
Half sovereigns, London	£300	£650
Half sovereigns, Southwark	£300	£650
Crowns, London	£350	£700
Crowns, Southwark	£450	£900
Halfcrowns, London	£300	£650
Halfcrowns, Southwark	£300	£650

Coinage in Edward's own name
First period 1547-49
Half sovereigns, Tower, read EDWARD 6	£450	£950

Edward VI sovereign, posthumous coinage

	F	VF
Half sovereigns, Southwark	£350	£850
Crown		unique
Halfcrowns		ext. rare

Second period 1549-50

	F	VF
Sovereigns	£1750	£4000
Half sovereigns, uncrowned bust London		ext. rare
Half sovereigns, SCUTUM on obv. ...	£500	£1250
Half sovereigns, Durham House, MDXL VII		ext. rare
Half sovereigns, crowned bust, London...	£500	£1250
Half sovereigns, half-length bust, Durham House	£4000	£8500
Crowns, uncrowned bust	£750	£1500
Crowns, crowned bust	£500	£1250
Halfcrowns, uncrowned bust	£550	£1250
Halfcrowns, crowned bust	£750	£1250

Edward VI fine sovereign of 30s third period

Third period 1550-53

	F	VF
'Fine' sovereigns of 30s, king enthroned	£7500	£18000
Sovereigns of 20s, half-length figure	£950	£2500
Half sovereigns, similar to last ...	£550	£1400
Crowns, similar but SCUTUM on rev	£650	£1600
Halfcrowns, similar	£750	£1800
Angels	£4000	£9000
Half angel		unique

MARY 1553-4

	F	VF
Sovereigns, different dates, some undated, some *mms*	£1600	£4000
Ryals, dated MDLII (1553)	£7500	£15000
Angels, *mm* pomegranate	£650	£1400
Half angels —	£2000	£6500

Mary Gold Sovereign of 1553

PHILIP AND MARY 1554-8

	F	VF
Angels, *mm* lis	£1250	£2750
Half angels —		ext. rare

Philip and Mary angel

ELIZABETH I 1558-1603
Hammered issues

	F	VF
'Fine' sovereigns of 30s, different issues from	£1500	£3500
Ryals	£3000	£9000
Angels, different issues	£290	£500
Half angels	£200	£450
Quarter angels —	£200	£400

Elizabeth I quarter angel

HAMMERED GOLD

	F	VF
Pounds of 20 shillings, only one issue	£600	£1250
Half pounds, different issues	£400	£850
Crowns —	£300	£650
Halfcrowns —	£250	£600

Elizabeth I hammered halfcrown

Milled issues

Half pounds, one issue but different marks	£700	£1800
Crowns —	£800	£2000
Halfcrowns —	£1200	£3000

The Stuart Kings

James I gold sovereign

JAMES I 1603-25
1st coinage 1603-4

	F	VF
Sovereigns of 20 shillings two bust	£800	£1800
Half sovereigns	£2000	£4000
Crowns	£800	£2500
Halfcrowns	£250	£700

2nd coinage 1604-19

Rose-ryals of 30 shillings	£750	£2000
Spur-ryals of 15 shillings	£2000	£4000
Angels	£500	£1250
Half angels	£1500	£4000
Unites, different busts	£200	£450
Double crowns —	£160	£400
Britain crowns —	£130	£275

James I Rose-ryal of 30 shillings

	F	VF
Halfcrowns —	£120	£240
Thistle crowns, varieties	£135	£275

James I Thistle crown

3rd coinage 1619-25

Rose-ryals, varieties	£950	£2500
Spur-ryals	£2200	£4500
Angels	£500	£1500
Laurels, different busts	£200	£450
Half laurels	£170	£350
Quarter laurels	£130	£220

James I laurel

CHARLES I 1625-49
Tower Mint 1625-43

Initial marks: lis, cross calvary, negro's head, castle, anchor, heart, plume, rose, harp, portcullis, bell, crown, tun, triangle, star, triangle in circle

		F	VF
Angels, varieties		£700	£1800
Angels, pierced as touchpieces	...	£400	£800
Unites —		£190	£400
Double crowns —		£170	£350
Crowns —		£120	£250

Tower Mint under Parliament 1643-8
Initial marks: (P), (R), eye, sun, sceptre

		F	VF
Unites, varieties		£300	£700
Double crowns —		£400	£900
Crowns —		£250	£475

Briot's milled issues 1631-2
Initial marks: anemone and **B**, daisy and **B**, **B**

		F	VF
Angels		£5000	*
Unites		£900	£2000
Double crowns		£550	£1500
Crowns		ext. rare	

Coins of provincial mints
Aberystwyth 1638-42

Unite		unique

Shrewsbury 1642

	F	VF
Triple unite (£3 piece)	£30000	£60000

Oxford 1642-46

		F	VF
Triple unites, varieties from		£2000	£4750
Unites —		£650	£1250
Half unites —		£500	£1000

Charles I Oxford triple unite, 1643

Bristol 1643-45

		F	VF
Unites		*	*
Half unites		ext. rare	

Truro 1642-43

Unites		ext. rare

Chester

Unites		*	*

Siege pieces 1645-49
Colchester besieged 1648

Ten shillings (**F**)		ext. rare

Pontefract besieged 1648-49

Unites (**F**)		ext. rare

Commonwealth 1649-60 gold unite

COMMONWEALTH 1649-60

			F	VF
Unites *im* sun			£400	£850
— *im* anchor			£1250	£3000
Double crowns *im* sun			£300	£700
— *im* anchor			£1000	£2500
Crowns *im* sun			£250	£550
— *im* anchor			£1250	*

Commonwealth crown

CHARLES II 1660-85
Hammered coinage 1660-62

Charles II gold unite

			F	VF
Unites, two issues from			£500	£1400
Double crowns —			£500	£1200
Crowns —			£450	£950

SILVER COINS

In this section column headings are mainly F (Fine) and VF (Very Fine), but for pennies of the early Plantagenets — a series in which higher-grade coins are seldom available — prices are shown under the headings Fair and F. Again it should be noted that throughout the section prices are approximate, for the commonest types only, and are the amounts collectors can expect to pay — not dealers' buying prices. Descriptions of some early Anglo-Saxon coins are, of necessity, brief because of pressure on space. Descriptions such as 'cross/moneyer's name' indicate that a cross appears on the obverse and the moneyer's name on the reverse. For more details see Standard Catalogue of British Coins — Volume 1 published by B. A. Seaby Ltd, and English Hammered Coins, Volumes 1 and 2, by J. J. North, published by Spink and Son Ltd. [A new edition of Volume 2 was published in 1991 and a new edition of Volume 1 was published in 1994.]

Anglo-Saxon Sceats and Stycas

Two superb sceats

EARLY PERIOD c 600-750	F	VF
Silver sceats ... ...from	£60	£150

A fascinating series with great variation of styles of early art. Large numbers of types and varieties.

NORTHUMBRIAN KINGS c 737-867

	F	VF
Silver sceats c 737-796 ... ...from	£150	£350
Copper stycas c 810-867 ... ...from	£10	£35

Struck for many kings. Numerous moneyers and different varieties. The copper styca is the commonest coin in the Anglo-Saxon series.

ARCHBISHOPS OF YORK c 732-900

	F	VF
Silver sceats ... ... from	£50	£150
Copper stycas	£35	£75

> From here onwards until the reign of Edward I all coins are silver pennies unless otherwise stated

Kings of Kent

HEABERHT c 764

	F	VF
Monogram/cross	ext. rare	

One moneyer (EOBA).

ECGBERHT c 765-780

Monogram/cross	£1700	£4000

Two moneyers (BABBA and UDD)

EADBERHT PRAEN 797-798

EADBERHT REX/moneyer	£2000	£4500

Three moneyers

Penny of Eadberht Praen

CUTHRED 789-807

Non-portrait, various designs ...from	£450	£950
Bust right	£550	£1250

Different moneyers, varieties etc.

BALDRED c 825

Bust right	£900	£2750
Cross/cross	£700	£2000

different types and moneyers

Baldred penny, bust right

ANONYMOUS c 823

	F	VF
Bust right	£600	£1700

Different varieties and moneyers.

Archbishops of Canterbury

JAENBERHT 766-792

	F	VF
Various types (non portrait) ...from	£1250	£2600

AETHELHEARD 793-805

Various types (non portrait) ...from	£1250	£2500

WULFRED 805-832

Various groups (portrait types) from	£600	£1250

CEOLNOTH 833-870

Various groups (portrait types) from	£300	£750

Ceolnoth penny

AETHERED 870-889

Various types (portrait, non-portrait)	ext. rare	

PLEGMUND 890-914

Various types (all non-portrait) from	£375	£900

Kings of Mercia

Offa portrait penny

OFFA 757-796

	F	VF
Non-portrait from	£350	£750
Portrait from	£550	£1250

Many types and varieties

Cynethryth (wife of Offa) portrait penny

CYNETHRYTH (wife of Offa)

	F	VF
Portrait	£2500	£5500
Non-portrait	£2500	£4500

COENWULF 796-821
Various types (portrait, non-portrait)from **£300 £650**

Coenwulf portrait penny

CEOLWULF I 821-823
Various types (portrait) **£650 £1600**

BEORNWULF 823-825
Various types (portrait) **£950 £2500**

Beornwulf penny

LUDICA 825-827
Two types (portrait) **(F)** ... ... ext. rare
(One was to be sold by Spink in October 1994.)

WIGLAF 827-829, 830-840
Two groups (portrait, non-portrait) **£1800 £4500**

BERHTWULF 840-852
Two groups
(portrait, non-portrait) **£750 £2000**

Beornwult penny

BURGRED 852-874
One type (portrait), five variants ... **£95 £200**

CEOLWULF II 874-c 877
Two types (portrait) ... ... **£3750** *

Kings of East Anglia

BEONNA c 758

	F	VF
Silver sceat	£450	£950

AETHELBERHT LUL (died 794)
Portrait type **(F)** ... ... ext. rare

Eadwald penny

EADWALD c 796

	F	VF
Non-portrait types	£1250	£3000

AETHELSTAN I c 850
Various types (portrait, non-portrait) **£375 £850**

AETHELWEARD c 850
Non-portrait types **£500 £1250**

EADMUND 855-870
Non-portrait types **£300 £650**

Viking Invaders 878-954

ALFRED

	F	VF
Imitations of Alfred pennies etc. from	£300	£550

(Many different types, portrait and non portrait)

ANGLIA
AETHELSTAN II 878-890
Cross/moneyer ... ... very rare

OSWALD (unknown in history except from coins)
A/cross ... ... ext. rare

ALFDENE (uncertain c 900)
Penny and halfpenny ... ... ext. rare

ST EADMUND
Memorial coinage, various
legends etc **£70 £160**
Many moneyers.
Halfpenny, similar **£400 £1250**

St Eadmund memorial penny

ST MARTIN OF LINCOLN c 925
Sword/cross ... ... **£2000** *

AETHELRED c 870
Temple/cross ... ... ext. rare

YORK
SIEVERT-SIEFRED-CNUT c 897
Crosslet/small cross **£80 £150**
Many different groups and varieties.
Halfpenny, similar **£400 £950**

EARL SIHTRIC (unknown)
Non-portrait ... ... ext. rare

REGNALD c 919-921
Various types, some blundered ... **£2000 £4500**

SIHTRIC I 921-927
Sword/cross ... ... ext. rare

ANLAF GUTHFRITHSSON 939-941
Raven/cross **£2750 £6000**
Cross/cross ... ... ext. rare
Flower/cross ... ... ext. rare

ANLAF SIHTRICSSON 941-944, 948-952   F   VF
Various types **£2000 £6000**

SIHTRIC II c 942-943
Shield/standard ... ...   ext. rare

REGNALD II c 941-943
Cross/cross ... ... **£3500**   *
Shield/standard ... ... **£3500**   *

ERIC BLOODAXE 948, 952-954
Cross/moneyer ... ... ext. rare
Sword/cross **£3250 £6500**

ST PETER OF YORK c 905-927
Various types ... ...from **£250 £650**
Halfpenny, similar ... ... **£750**   *

Kings of Wessex

BEORHTRIC 786-802   F   VF
Two types (non-portrait) ... ... ext. rare

Ecgberht penny

ECGBERHT 802-839
FOUR GROUPS (portrait, non-portrait **£850 £2500**
Mints of Canterbury, London, Rochester, Winchester

AETHELWULF 839-858
Four phases (portrait, non-portrait) from **£250 £575**
Mints of Canterbury, Rochester (?)

AETHELBERHT 858-866
Two types (portrait) ... ...from **£220 £500**
Many moneyers.

AETHELRED I 865-871
Portrait types ... ...from **£235 £700**
Many moneyers.

ALFRED THE GREAT 871-899
Portrait in style of Aethelred I **£350 £800**
Four other portrait types the commonest being those
  with the London monogram reverse **£650 £1500**
Halfpennies **£800 £2000**

Alfred the Great penny, London monogram

Non-portrait types ... ... from **£220 £475**
Many different styles of lettering etc.
Halfpennies **£650 £1500**

EDWARD THE ELDER 899-924
Non-portrait types:
Cross/moneyer's name in two lines **£130 £275**
Halfpennies as previous ... ... ext. rare

Rare penny of Edward the Elder

Portrait types: F   VF
Bust/moneyer's name... ... ... **£350 £950**
Many types, varieties and moneyers.

Kings of all England

AETHELSTAN 924-39   F   VF
Non-portrait types:
  Cross/moneyer's name in two lines **£200 £450**
  Crosscross **£200 £400**

Portrait types:
bust/moneyer's name **£450 £1400**
Bust/small cross **£500 £1300**
Many other issues. There are also different mints
and many moneyer's names.

Aethelstan portrait penny

EADMUND 939-46
Non-portrait types:
Cross or rosette/moneyer's name
  in two lines **£170 £450**
Silver halfpenny, similar **£800 £2000**

Eadmund penny, two-line type

Portrait types:
Crowned bust/small cross **£300 £1250**
Helmeted bust/cross crosslet **£750 £2500**
Many other issues and varieties; also different mint
names and moneyers.

EADRED 946-55
Non-portrait types:
Cross/moneyer's name in two line ... **£130 £325**
Silver halfpenny, similar **£800 £1600**
Rosette/moneyer's name **£150 £400**

Eadred penny, portrait type

	F	VF
Portrait types:		
Crowned bust/small cross...	**£350**	**£1200**
Again many variations and mint names and moneyers.		

HOWEL DDA (King of Wales), died c 948
| Small cross/moneyer's name in two lines (GILLYS) ... ... | | unique |

EADWIG 955-59
Non-portait types:
Cross/moneyer's name ... ...from	**£190**	**£500**
Many variations, some rare.		
Silver halfpennies, similar		ext. rare

Portrait types:
| Bust/cross ... ... | | ext. rare |

EADGAR 959-75
Non-portrait types:
Cross/moneyer's name ... ...from	**£110**	**£260**
Cross/cross ... ...from	**£110**	**£220**
Rosette/rosette ... ...from	**£150**	**£300**
Halfpennies		ext. rare

Eadgar non-portrait penny

Portrait types:
Pre-Reform	**£400**	**£1250**
Halfpenny, diademed bust/London monogram	**£2500**	**£6500**
Post Reform	**£475**	**£1000**
Many other varieties.		

EDWARD THE MARTYR 975-78
Portrait type:
| Bust left/small cross ... ... | **£650** | **£1500** |
| Many different mints and moneyers. | | |

AETHELRED II 1978-1016
First small cross ... ... from	**£400**	**£1250**
First hand ... ... from	**£90**	**£200**
Second hand ... ... from	**£70**	**£135**
Benediction hand ... ... from	**£450**	**£1200**
CRUX... ... ... from	**£70**	**£130**

Aethelred II CRUX type penny

	F	VF
Long Cross	**£75**	**£120**
Helmet	**£85**	**£150**
Agnus Dei		ext. rare
Other issues and varieties; many mint names and moneyers.		

Aethelred II long cross penny

CNUT 1016-35
| Quatrefoil ... ...from | **£80** | **£140** |

Cnut quatrefoil type penny

| Pointed helmet ... ...from | **£80** | **£140** |

Cnut pointed helmet type

Small cross ... ...from	**£75**	**£110**
Jewel cross ... ...from	**£650**	*
Other types, and many different mint names and moneyers.		

HAROLD 1 1035-40
Jewel cross ... ...from	**£190**	**£450**
Long cross with trefoils ... ...from	**£150**	**£350**
Long cross with fleurs-de-lis ...from	**£150**	**£350**
Many different mint names and moneyers.		

HARTHACNUT 1035-42
Jewel cross, bust left	**£750**	**£1800**
— bust right	**£700**	**£1600**
Arm and sceptre types	**£800**	**£1700**
Different mint names and moneyers.		
Scandinavian types struck at Lund ...	**£190**	**£400**

EDWARD THE CONFESSOR 1042-66
PACX type ... ...from	**£150**	**£450**
Radiate crown/small cross ...from	**£80**	**£150**
Trefoil quadrileteral ... ...from	**£75**	**£140**
Small flan ... ...from	**£70**	**£115**
Expanding cross types ... ...from	**£85**	**£140**

Edward the Confessor expanding cross penny

	F	VF
Pointed helmet types	£75	£135
Sovereign/eagles	£90	£175
Hammer cross	£75	£130
Bust facing	£80	£120
Cross and piles	£80	£150
Large bust, facing, with sceptre ...	£1000	£2500

Other issues, including a unique gold penny; many different mint names and moneyers.

HAROLD II 1066
Crowned head left with sceptre ...	£350	£650

Harold II, bust left, without sceptre

	F	VF
Similar but no sceptre	£400	£800
Crowned head right with sceptre ...	£750	£1500

The Norman Kings

WILLIAM I 1066-87
		F	VF
Profile/cross fleury ... ...from		£135	£350
Bonnet ... ...from		£110	£200
Canopy ... ...from		£200	£400
Two sceptres ... ...from		£135	£350
Two stars ... ...from		£120	£200
Sword ... ...from		£200	£450

William I profile/cross and trefoils

		F	VF
Profile/cross and trefoils ... ...from		£300	£650
PAXS ... ...from		£95	£150

WILLIAM II 1087-1100
		F	VF
Profile ... ... from		£270	£575
Cross in quatrefoil ... ... from		£220	£475
Cross voided ... ... from		£220	£550
Cross pattee over fleury ... from		£350	£700
Cross fleury and piles ... from		£450	£950

Henry I annulets type

HENRY I 1100-1135
		F	
Annulets ... ...from		£250	*
Profile/cross fleury ... ...from		£200	*
PAX ... ...from		£250	*
Annulets and piles ... ...from		£300	*
Voided cross and fleurs ... ...from		£500	*
Pointing bust and stars ... ...from		£650	*
Quatrefoil and piles ... ...from		£275	*
Profile/cross and annulets ...from		£600	*
Cross in quatrefoil ... ...from		£470	*

	F	VF
Full face/cross fleury	£170	*
Double inscription	£375	*
Small bust/cross and annulets ...	£250	*
Star in lozenge fleury	£250	*
Pellets in quatrefoil	£120	£275
Quadrilateral on cross fleury	£110	£200
Halfpennies	£1700	£3500

STEPHEN 1135-54
		F	VF
Cross moline (Watford) ... ...from		£90	£160

Stephen 'Watford' penny

	F	VF
Cross moline PERERIC	£325	£750
Voided cross and mullets	£200	£450

Stephen penny, voided cross pattée with mullets

	F	VF
Profile/cross fleury	£375	£900
Voided cross pommée (Awbridge)	£250	£450

There are also a number of irregular issues produced during the civil war, all of which are very rare. These include several extremely rare and attractive pieces bearing the names of barons, such as Eustace Fitzjohn and Robert de Stuteville.

The Plantagenet Kings

HENRY II 1154-89
	Fair	F
Cross and crosslets ('Tealby' coinage)	£25	£50

The issue is classified by bust variants into six groups, struck at 32 mints.

Henry II Tealby penny

	F	VF
Short cross pennies	£30	£70

The 'short cross' coinage was introduced in 1180 and continued through successive reigns until Henry III brought about a change in 1247. HENRICVS REX appears on all these coins but they can be classified into reigns by the styles of the busts and lettering.

RICHARD I 1189-99
	F	VF
Short cross pennies	£35	£80

HAMMERED SILVER

JOHN 1199-1216
Short cross pennies **£30** **£70**

John short cross penny

HENRY III 1216-72
Short cross pennies	£15	£35
Long cross pennies no sceptre... ...	£12	£35
Long cross pennies with sceptre ...	£12	£35

Henry III long cross penny, no sceptre

The 'long cross' pennies, first introduced in 1247, are divided into two groups: those with sceptre and those without. They also fall into five basic classes, with many varieties.

EDWARD I 1272-1307
1st coinage 1272-78
Long cross pennies ... ...from **£25** **£80**
similar in style to those of Henry III but with more realistic beard.

Edward I Durham penny

New coinage 1278-1307
Groats	£1000	£2750
Pennies, various classes, mints from	£10	£30
Halfpennies— ... ...from	£25	£65
Farthings — ... ...from	£65	£160

EDWARD II 1307-27
Pennies, various classes, mints from	£12	£50
Halfpennies ... ...from	£50	£125
Farthings ... ...from	£65	£160

EDWARD III 1327-77
1st and 2nd coinages 1327-43
Pennies (only 1st coinage) various types and mints	£200	£450
Halfpennies, different types and mints	£50	£150
Farthings	£70	£150

3rd coinage 1344-51 [Florin Coinage]
Pennies, various types and mints ...	£15	£65
Halfpennies —	£15	£60
Farthings	£70	£150

A superb Edward III penny

4th coinage 1351-77

	F	VF
Groats, many types and mints from...	£25	£90

Edward III groat

Halfgroats —	£20	£70
Pennies —	£12	£45
Halfpennies, different types	£80	£170
Farthings, a few types	£100	£350

Richard II groat

RICHARD II 1377-99
Groats, four types from	£200	£500
Halfgroats	£190	£450
Pennies, various types, London ...	£170	£450
Pennies, various types, York	£50	£120
Pennies, Durham	£190	*
Halfpennies, three main types ...	£30	£80
Farthings, some varieties	£190	£450

HENRY IV 1399-1413
Groats, varieties from	£1500	£4500
Halfgroats —	£500	£1600
Pennies —	£250	£750
Halfpennies —	£200	£475
Farthings —	£500	*

Henry V groat

HENRY V 1413-22
Groats, varieties from	£60	£140

	F	VF
Halfgroats	£70	£160
Pennies	£35	£90
Halfpennies	£30	£90
Farthings	£160	£375

HENRY VI 1422-61
Annulet issue 1422-1427

	F	VF
Groats	£20	£65
Halfgroats	£20	£60
Pennies	£20	£50
Halfpennies	£20	£50
Farthings	£160	£350

Rosette-Mascle issue 1427-1430

	F	VF
Groats	£30	£100
Halfgroats	£30	£70
Pennies	£30	£70
Halfpennies	£20	£50
Farthings	£120	£250

Pinecone-Mascle 1430-1434

	F	VF
Groats	£30	£90
Halfgroats	£25	£70
Pennies	£20	£50
Halfpennies	£25	£50
Farthings	£120	£250

Leaf-Mascle 1434-1435

	F	VF
Groats	£50	£150
Halfgroats	£30	£90
Pennies	£30	£90
Halfpennies	£25	£50

Leaf-Trefoil 1435-1438

	F	VF
Groats	£40	£125
Halfgroats	£30	£80
Pennies	£25	£70
Halfpennies	£25	£60
Farthings	£120	£250

Trefoil 1438-1443

	F	VF
Groats	£60	£140
Halfgroats	£250	£650
Halfpennies	£40	£90

Trefoil-Pellet 1443-1445

	F	VF
Groats	£50	£170

Leaf-Pellet 1445-1454

	F	VF
Groats	£40	£140
Halfgroats	£40	£90
Pennies	£40	£90
Halfpennies	£30	£60
Farthings	£150	£300

Unmarked 1445-1454

	F	VF
Groats	£200	£650
Halfgroats	£200	£450

Cross-Pellet 1454-1460

	F	VF
Groats	£90	£250
Halfgroats	£190	£450
Pennies	£60	£120
Halfpennies	£60	£120
Farthings	£150	*

Lis-Pellet 1454-1460

	F	VF
Groats	£175	£450

There are many different varieties, mintmarks and mints in this reign. These prices are for the commonest pieces in each issue.

HAMMERED SILVER

EDWARD IV 1st Reign 1461-1470
Heavy coinage 1461-4

	F	VF
Groats, many classes, all London ...	£70	£180
Halfgroats, many classes, all London	£250	*
Pennies, different classes. London, York and Durham	£150	*
Halfpennies, different classes, all London	£60	*
Farthing, one type. London	£600	*

Light coinage 1464-70

	F	VF
Groats, many different issues, varieties, mms and mints from ...	£30	£80
Halfgroats, ditto	£35	£65
Pennies, ditto	£30	£65
Halfpennies, ditto	£40	£80
Farthings Two issues	£400	*

HENRY VI (restored) 1470-71

	F	VF
Groats, different mints, mms from ...	£120	£250
Halfgroats — from	£250	£500
Pennies — from	£220	£500
Halfpennies — from	£200	£450

EDWARD IV 2nd reign 1471-83

	F	VF
Groats, different varieties, mints etc	£35	£85
Halfgroats	£30	£70
Pennies	£30	£75
Halfpennies	£25	£70

EDWARD V 1483
(The coins read EDWARD but are now considered to be attributable to Richard III)
(Mintmark boar's head)

	F	VF
Groats	£1900	*
Halfgroats (?)		
Penny (?)		

RICHARD III 1483-85

	F	VF
Groats, London and York mints, various combinations of mms ...	£220	£475
Halfgroats	£700	£1400
Pennies, York and Durham (London mint unique)	£250	£500
Halfpennies	£250	£500

PERKIN WARBECK, PRETENDER

	F	VF
Groat, 1494 [cf. BNJ XXVI, p. 125] ...	£600	£2000

The Tudor Monarchs
HENRY VII 1485-1509

Facing bust issues:

	F	VF
Groats, all London		
Open crown without arches ...	£75	£250
Crown with two arches unjewelled	£50	£100
Crown with two jewelled arches ...	£55	£120
Similar but only one arch jewelled	£35	£80
Similar but tall thin lettering ...	£40	£110
Similar but single arch, tall thin lettering	£40	£90
Halfgroats, London		
Open crown without arches, tressure unbroken	£300	£700
Double arched crown	£50	£175
Unarched crown	£35	£70
Some varieties and different mms.		
Halfgroats, Canterbury		
Open crown, without arches ...	£35	£80
Double arched crown	£30	£65
Some varieties and different mms.		

HAMMERED SILVER

	F	VF
Halfgroats, York		
Double arched crown	£35	£80
Unarched crown with tressure broken	£30	£70
Double arched crown with keys at side of bust	£25	£60
Many varieties and different *mms*.		
Pennies, facing bust type		
London		rare
Canterbury, open crown		rare
—arched crown	£45	£120
Durham, Bishop Sherwood (S on breast)	£60	£200
York	£40	£90
Many varieties and *mms*.		
Pennies, 'sovereign enthroned' type		
London, many varieties...	£35	£90
Durham —...	£45	£120
York —...	£35	£90
Halfpennies, London		
Open crown	£65	£150
Arched crown	£35	£120
Crown with lower arch	£25	£100
Some varieties and *mms*.		
Halfpennies, Canterbury		
Open crown	£150	*
Arched crown	£150	*
Halfpennies, York		
Arched crown and key below bust	£120	£250
Farthings, all London	£250	*

Profile issues:
Testoons *im* lis, three different legends £3500 £8000

Henry VII profile issue testoon

	F	VF
Groats, all London		
Tentative issue (doubled band to crown)	£130	£400
Regular issue (triple band to crown)	£40	£140
Some varieties, and *mms*.		
Halfgroats		
London	£45	£140
—no numeral after king's name ...	£200	£700
Canterbury	£30	£80
York, two keys below shield ...	£30	£75
—XB by shield	£500	*

HENRY VIII 1509-47
With portrait of Henry VII
1st coinage 1509-26

	F	VF
Groats, London	£80	£240
Groats, Tournai	£300	£850

	F	VF
Groats, Tournai, without portrait ...	£1500	*
Halfgroats, London	£60	£175
Halfgroats, Canterbury, varieties ...	£40	£120

Henry VIII first coinage halfgroat, Canterbury

	F	VF
Halfgroats, York, varieties...	£35	£120
Halfgroat, Tournai		unique
Pennies, 'sovereign enthroned' type, London	£35	£90
Pennies, Canterbury, varieties... ...	£75	*
Pennies, Durham, varieties	£40	£100
Halfpennies, facing bust type,		
London	£50	*
Canterbury	£70	*
Farthings, portcullis type, London ...	£400	£900

Two Henry VIII second coinage groats, one early, one late portrait

With young portrait of Henry VIII
2nd coinage 1526-44

	F	VF
Groats, London, varieties, *mms* ...	£35	£120
Groats, Irish title, HIB REX...	£350	£850
Groats, York *mms*	£70	£200
Halfgroats, London *mms*	£35	£90
Halfgroats, Canterbury *mms*	£30	£80
Halfgroats, York *mms*...	£30	£80
Pennies, 'sovereign enthround' type		
London, varieties, *mms*...	£30	£90
Canterbury, varieties, *mms*	£60	*
Durham—	£30	£90
York	£90	£200
Halfpennies, facing bust type		
London, varieties, *mms*...	£45	£120
Canterbury	£60	£150
York	£70	£140
Farthings, portcullis type	£450	£950

With old bearded portrait
3rd coinage 1544-47
Posthumous issues 1547-51
Testoons (or shillings)

	F	VF
London (Tower mint), varieties, *mms*	£400	£950
Southwark, varieties, *mms* ...	£400	£950
Bristol, varieties, *mms*	£475	£1200
Groats, six different busts, varieties, *mms*		
London (Tower mint)	£50	£160
Southwark	£50	£160
Bristol...	£65	£200
Canterbury	£65	£200
London (Durham House)	£170	£600

Henry VIII third coinage groat

Halfgroats, only one style of
bust (except York which has
two), varieties, *mms*

	F	VF
London (Tower mint)	£45	£140
Southwark...	£70	£250
Bristol...	£65	£180
Canterbury	£35	£130
York	£60	£160
London (Durham House)	very rare	

Pennies (facing bust) varieties, *mms*

London (Tower mint)	£40	£120
Southwark	£75	£175
London (Durham House)	very rare	
Bristol	£50	£160
Canterbury	£40	£140
York	£45	£140

Halfpennies (facing bust) varieties, *mms*

London (Tower mint)	£50	£150
Bristol	£90	£200
Canterbury	£50	£120
York	£40	£120

EDWARD VI 1547-53
1st period 1547-49

	F	VF
Shillings, London (Durham House), *mm* bow, patterns (?)	*	*
Groats, London (Tower), *mm* arrow	£400	£900
Groats, London (Southwark) *mm* E, none	£425	£1200
Halfgroats, London (Tower), *mm* arrow	£350	£800
Halfgroats, London (Southwark), *mm* arrow, E	£350	£750
Halfgroats, Canterbury, *mm* none ...	£200	£600
Pennies, London (Tower), *mm*	£275	£650
Pennies, London (Southwark), *mm* E	£295	£700
Pennies, Bristol, *mm* none	£200	£600
Halfpennies, London (Tower), *mm* uncertain	£450	£1000
Halfpennies, Bristol, *mm* none ...	£300	£650

Edward VI 2nd period shilling. Tower mint

	F	VF

2nd period 1549-50

	F	VF
Shillings, London (Tower) various *mms*	£95	£300
Shillings, Bristol, *mm* TC	£600	£1300
Shillings, Canterbury, *mm* T or t ...	£100	£400
Shillings, London (Durham House), *mm* bow, varieties	£250	£650

3rd period £550-53
Base silver (similar to issues of 2nd period)

Shillings, London (Tower), *mm* lis, lion, rose	£130	£350
Pennies, London (Tower), *mm* escallop	£90	£250
Pennies, York, *mm* mullet	£75	£250
Halfpennies, London (Tower)	£275	£650

Fine Silver

Crown 1551 *mm* Y, 1551-53 *mm* tun	£230	£500
Halfcrown, walking horse, 1551, *mm* Y	£150	£450
Halfcrowns, galloping horse, 1551-52, *mm* tun	£200	£900

Edward VI 1552 halfcrown, galloping horse

Halfcrowns, walking horse, 1553, *mm* tun	£650	£1500
Shillings, *mm* Y, tun	£50	£170
Sixpences, London (Tower), *mm* Y, tun	£55	£170
Sixpences, York, *mm* mullet	£100	£350
Threepences, London (Tower), *mm* tun	£125	£450
Threepences, York *mm* mullet ...	£250	£650
Pennies, sovereign type	£600	£1500
Farthings, portcullis type	£700	£1250

Mary groat, pomegranate after MARIA

MARY 1553-54

Groats, *mm* pomegranate	£55	£175
Halfgroats, similar	£550	*
Pennies, rev VERITAS TEMP FILIA ...	£400	*
Pennies, rev CIVITAS LONDON	£400	*

HAMMERED SILVER

PHILIP AND MARY 1554-58

	F	VF
Shillings, full titles, without date	£120	£400
— also without XII	£150	£600
— dated 1554	£125	£450
— dated 1554, English titles	£140	£600
— dated 1555, English titles only	£170	£500
— dated 1554, English titles only, also without XII	£300	*
— 1554 but date below bust	£350	*
— 1555 but date below bust	£350	*
— 1555 similar to previous but without ANGL	£450	*
Sixpences, full titles, 1554	£120	£400
— full titles, undated	*	*
— English titles, 1555	£130	£400
— similar but date below bust, 1554	£500	*
— English titles, 1557	£150	£550
— similar, but date below bust, 1557	£650	*
Groats, mm lis	£50	£200
Halfgroats, mm lis	£450	£1250

Philip and Mary penny

	F	VF
Pennies, mm lis	£400	*
Base pennies, without portrait	£50	£160

ELIZABETH I 1558-1603
Hammered coinage, 1st issue 1558-61
Shillings ELIZABETH

	F	VF
Wire-line inner circles	£250	£750
Beaded inner circles	£100	£320
ET for Z	£50	£160

Edward VI shilling greyhound countermark (reign of Elizabeth), and Elizabeth I hammered groat

	F	VF
Groats		
Wire-line inner circles	£110	£375
Beaded inner circles	£45	£140
ET for Z	£30	£130
Halfgroats		
Wire-line inner circles	£150	£350
Beaded inner circles	£30	£75
Pennies		
Wire-line inner circles	£140	£380
Beaded inner circles	£15	£60
Countermarked shillings of Edward VI, 1560-61		
With portcullis mark (Current for 4½d)	£1250	*
With greyhound mark (current for 2½d)	£1350	*

Hammered coinage, 2nd issue 1561-82

	F	VF
Sixpences, dated 1561-82	£30	£95
Threepences, 1561-82	£20	£75
Halfgroats, undated	£30	£90
Threehalfpences, 1561-62, 1564-70, 1572-79, 1581-82	£25	£90
Pennies, undated	£20	£70
Threefarthings, 1561-62, 1568, 1572-78, 1581-82	£60	£150

Elizabeth I Crown

Hammered coinage, 3rd issue 1583-1603

	F	VF
Crowns, im 1	£370	£850
Crowns, im 2	£450	£1350
Halfcrowns, im 1	£200	£550
Halfcrowns, im 2 (F)	£800	£2000
shillings ELIZAB	£45	£170
Sixpences, 1582-1602	£30	£130
Halfgroats, E D G ROSA etc	£15	£80
pennies	£15	£80
Halfpennies, portcullis type	£25	£80

There are many different mintmarks, such as lis, bell, lion etc., featured on the hammered coins of Elizabeth I, and these marks enable one to date those coins which are not themselves dated. For more details see J. J. North's English Hammered Coinage, Volume 2.

Milled Coinage

	F	VF
Shillings		
large size	£275	£750
Intermediate	£130	£450
Small	£110	£350
Sixpences		
1561	£35	£120
1562	£30	£100
1563-64, 1566	£55	£180
1567-68	£55	£180
1570-71	£85	£250
Groats, undated	£120	£400
Threepences, 1561, 1562-64	£100	£300
Halfgroats	£90	£300
Threefarthings	ext. rare	

The Stuart Kings

JAMES 1 1603-25
1st coinage 1603-04

	F	VF
Crowns, rev EXURGAT etc	£380	£900
Halfcrowns—	£450	£1000
Shillings, varieties	£45	£180
Sixpences, dated 1603-04, varieties	£30	£140
Halfgroats, undated	£25	£75
Pennies—	£30	£80

2nd coinage 1604-19	F	VF
Crowns rev QVAE DEVS etc	£300	£675
Halfcrowns —	£500	£1200

James I 2nd coinage shilling

	F	VF
Shillings, varieties	£35	£150
Sixpences, dated 1604-15, varieties etc.	£30	£95
Halfgroats, varieties	£15	£60
Pennies	£12	£40
Halfpennies	£15	£45

3rd coinage 1619-25

Crowns	£200	£500
—Plume over reverse shield	£220	£575
Halfcrowns	£100	£250
—Plume over reverse shield... ...	£160	£400

James I halfcrown (reverse) plume over shield

Shillings...	£30	£150
—Plume over reverse shield	£50	£200
Sixpences dated 1621-24	£30	£95
Halfgroats	£12	£30
Pennies	£12	£25
Halfpennies	£12	£40

James I sixpence of 1622

CHARLES I 1625-1649
Tower Mint 1625-1643
Crowns
(Obv. King on horseback. Rev. shield)

	F	VF
1st horseman/square shield im lis, cross calvary...	£200	£500
As last/plume above shield im list, cross calvary, castle ...	£480	£900
2nd horseman/oval shield im plume, rose, harp. Some varieties, from	£160	£450

	F	VF
3rd horseman/round shield im bell, crown, tun, anchor, triangle, star, portcullis, triangle in circle. Some varieties, from ...	£175	£450

Halfcrowns
(Obv. King on horseback. Rev. shield)

1st horseman/square shield im lis, cross calvary, negro's head, castle, anchor. Many varieties, from	£95	£300
2nd horseman/oval shield im plume, rose, harp, portcullis. Many varieties, from ...	£80	£200
3rd horseman/round shield im bell, crown, tun, portcullis, anchor, triangle, star Many varieties, from	£55	£140
4th horseman/round shield im star, triangle in circle	£35	£100

Charles I Tower halfcrown: first horsemen

Shillings

1st bust/square shield im lis, cross calvary Some varieties	£50	£160
2nd bust/square shield 2nd bust/square shield im cross calvary, negro's head, castle, anchor, heart, plume Many varieties, from	£45	£140
3rd bust/oval shield im plume, rose	£35	£120
4th bust/oval or round shield im harp, portcullis, bell, crown, tun Many varieties, from	£40	£140
5th bust/aquare shield im tun, anchor, triangle Many varieties, from	£30	£120
6th bust/square shield im anchor, triangle, star, triangle in circle Some varieties, from	£30	£120

Sixpences
(early ones are dated)

1st bust/square sheild, date above 1625 im lis, cross calvary 1626 im cross calvary	£45	£170
2nd bust/square shield, data above 1625, 1626 im cross calvary 1626, 1627 im negro's head 1626, 1628 im castle 1628, 1629 im anchor 1629 im heart 1630 im heart, plume	£60	£160
3rd bust/oval shield im plume, rose	£40	£150
4th bust/oval or round shield im harp, portcullis, bell, crown, tun	£30	£120

Charles I Tower sixpence mm bell

	F	VF
5th bust/square shield		
im tun, anchor, triangle		
Many varieties, from	£30	£130
6th bust/square shield		
im triangle, star	£30	£130
Halfgroats		
Crowned rose both sides		
im lis, cross calvary,		
blackamoor's head	£15	£50
2nd bust/oval shield		
im plume, rose	£18	£60
3rd bust/oval shield		
im rose, plume	£15	£60
4th bust/oval or round shield,		
im harp, crown, portcullis, bell,		
tun, anchor, triangle, star		
Many varieties, from	£15	£60
5th bust/round shield		
im anchor	£25	£100
Pennies		
Uncrowned rose both sides		
im one or two pellets, lis,		
negro's head	£12	£40
2nd bust/oval shield		
im plume	£15	£60
3rd bust/oval shield		
im plume, rose	£15	£60
4th bust/oval shield		
im harp, one or two pellets,		
portcullis, bell, triangle	£15	£60
5th bust/oval shield		
im one or two pellets, none	£15	£45
Halfpennies		
Uncrowned rose both sides		
im none	£15	£45

Tower Mint, under Parliament 1643-48
Crowns
(Obv. King on horseback, Rev. shield)

	F	VF
4th horseman/round shield		
im (P), (R), eye sun	£200	£500
5th horseman/round shield		
im sun, sceptre	£200	£600
Halfcrowns		
(Obv. King on horseback, Rev. shield)		
3rd horseman/round shield		
im (P), (R), eye, sun	£70	£275

Charles I Parliament shilling, mm eye

	F	VF
4th horseman/round shield		
im (P)	£150	*
5th horseman (tall)/round shield		
im sun, sceptre	£75	£300
Shillings (revs. all square shield)		
6th bust (crude)		
im (P), (R), eye, sun	£40	£200
7th bust (tall, slim)		
im sun, sceptre	£40	£200
8th bust (shorter, older)		
im sceptre	£40	£250
Sixpences (revs. all square shield)		
6th bust		
im (P), (R), eye, sun	£80	£200
7th bust		
im (R), eye, sun, sceptre	£75	£200
8th bust, (crude style)		
im eye, sun	*	*
Halfgroats		
4th bust/round shield		
im (P), (R), eye, sceptre	£30	£80
7th bust (old/round shield		
im eye, sun, sceptre	£25	£70
Pennies		
7th bust/oval shield		
im one or two pellets	£20	£50

Charles I Briot's crown

Briot's 1st milled issued 1631-32
im: flower and **B**

	F	VF
Crowns	£275	£800
Halfcrowns	£190	£480
Shillings	£120	£300
Sixpences	£70	£200
Halfgroats	£35	£70
Pennies	£30	£70

Briot's 2nd milled issue 1638-39
im: anchor, anchor and B, anchor and mullet

	F	VF
Halfcrowns	£160	£380
Shillings	£80	£200
Sixpences	£40	£100

Sixpence of Briot's 2nd milled issue

Briot's hammered issues 1638-39	F	VF
im: anchor, triangle over anchor		
Halfcrowns	£600	£1250
Shillings	£350	£900

	F	VF
Sixpences —...	£100	£300
Groats —	£50	£160
Threepences —	£40	£150
Halfgroats —	£80	£200
Pennies —	£100	£250

Charles I
halfcrown
of York

Bristol 1643-45
im: Bristol monogram, acorn, plumelet
Halfcrowns, varieties from	£130	£350

Bristol shilling

Shillings —	£100	£250
Sixpences —	£150	£400
Groats —	£120	£280
Threepences —	£120	£400
Halfgroats	£200	£450
Pennies	£275	£800

A, B, and plumes issues
*Associated with Thomas Bushell; previously
assigned to Lundy*
Halfcrowns, varieties from...	£400	£1250
Shillings —	£250	£650
Sixpences —...	£150	£400
Groats —...	£90	£200
Threepences	£80	£170
Halfgroats	£275	£700

Truro 1642-43
im: rose, bugle
Crowns, varieties	£180	£450
Halfcrowns —	£375	£750
Shillings —	ext. rare	

Truro or Exeter
im: rose
Halfcrowns, varieties	£100	£300

PROVINCIAL MINTS
York 1642-44
im: lion
Halfcrowns, varieties from	£90	£250
Shillings —	£75	£200
Sixpences —	£150	£375
Threepences...	£40	£95

Aberystwyth 1638-42
im: open book
Halfcrowns, varieties from	£375	£900
Shillings —	£170	£450
Sixpences —...	£180	£500
Groats —	£35	£80

Aberystwyth groat

Threepences —	£25	£60
Halfgroats —	£35	£90
Pennies —	£70	£200
Halfpennies	£150	£350

Aberystwyth – Furnace 1647-48
im: crown
Halfcrowns from	£1000	£2500
Shillings	ext. rare	
Sixpences	£1250	*
Groats	£200	£450
Threepences	£250	£600
Halfgroats	£250	£600
Pennies	£600	£1250

Shrewsbury 1642
mm: plume without band
Pounds, varieties from	£800	£3000
Halfpounds —	£375	£900
Crowns —	£300	£800
Halfcrowns —	£220	£600
Shillings —	£450	£1250

Oxford 1642-46
mm: plume, with band
Pounds, varieties from	£800	£3000
Halfpounds—	£300	£600
Crowns—	£300	£650
Halfcrowns—	£70	£200
Shillings—	£75	£200

*Truro
crown*

Exeter 1643-46
im Ex, rose, castle
Halfpounds	ext. rare	
Crowns, varieties	£130	£400

		F	VF
Halfcrowns —	... ...	£160	£350
Shillings —	... ...	£160	£450
Sixpences —	... ...	£150	£500
Groats	... ...	£60	£175
Threepences	... ...	£70	£180
Halfgroats —	... ...	£120	£350
Pennies	... ...	£200	£450

Worcester 1643-4
im: castle, helmet, leopard's head, lion, two lions, lis, rose, star

Halfcrowns, many varieties	£350	£850

Salopia (Shrewsbury) 1644
im: helmet, lis, rose (in legend)

Halfcrowns, many varieties	£500	£2000

Worcester or Salopia (Shrewsbury)
im: bird, boar's head, lis, castle, cross, and annulets, helmet, lion, lis, pear, rose, scroll

Shillings, varieties	... ...	£450	£1750
Sixpences	... ...	£800	£1500
Groats	... ...	£400	£1250
Threepences	... ...	£300	£850
Halfgroats	... ...	£350	£900

'HC' mint (probably Hartlebury Castle, Worcester 1646)
im: pear, three pears

Halfcrowns	... ...	£1000	£3000

Chester 1644
im: cinquefoil, plume, prostrate gerb, three gerbs

Halfcrowns, varieties	£500	£1250
Shillings	... ...	£2000	*
Threepences	... ...	very rare	

SIEGE PIECES
Carlisle besieged 1644-45

Three shillings	... ...	£2500	£5500
Shillings (F)	... ...	£1700	£3500

Carlisle siege shilling

Newark besieged many times
(surrendered May 6, 1646)

Halfcrowns, 1645-46 (F)	... ...	£300	£750

Newark siege halfcrown

Shillings, 1645-46, varieties (F)	...	£200	£600
Ninepences, 1645-46	... ...	£200	£550
Sixpences	... ...	£190	£650

Pontefract besieged 1648-49

		F	VF
Two shillings, 1648	... ...		ext. rare
Shillings, 1648, varieties	... ...	£575	£1250

Pontefract siege shilling

Scarborough besieged 1644-45
Many odd values issued here, all of which are extremely rare. The coin's value was decided by the intrinsic value of the piece of metal from which it was made.
Examples: 5s. 8d, 2s 4d, 1s 9d, 1s 3d, 7d etc (F).
Collectors could expect to pay at least £2000 or more in F and £4000 in VF for any of these.

COMMONWEALTH 1649-60

Crowns, *im* sun 1649, 51-54, 56	...	£300	£600
Halfcrowns, *im* sun 1649, 1651-6	...	£120	£350
— *im* anchor 1658-60		£400	*
Shillings, *im* sun 1649, 1661-87	...	£60	£170
—*im* anchor 1658-60	...	£350	*

A superb 1651 sixpence

Sixpences, *im* sun 1649, 1651-7	...	£70	£150
— *im* anchor 1658-60		£400	*
Halfgroats undated	... ...	£20	£60
Pennies undated ...	... ...	£20	£50
Halfpennies undated	... ...	£20	£60

CHARLES II 1660-85
Hammered coinage 1660-62

Halfcrowns, three issues ...	...from	£200	£500
Shillings —	... ...	...from	£80	£350

Charles II hammered issue shilling

Sixpences —	... ...	£60	£200
Fourpences, third issue only	...	£20	£70
Threepences —	...from	£20	£65
Twopences, three issues ...	...from	£10	£50
Pennies —	...from	£20	£50

'ROYAL' AND 'ROSE' BASE METAL FARTHINGS

Until 1613 English coins were struck only in gold or silver — the monarchy considered that base metal issues would be discreditable to the royal prerogative of coining. However, silver coins had become far too small, farthings so tiny that they had to be discontinued. So to meet demands for small change James I authorised Lord Harington to issue copper farthing tokens. Subsequently this authority passed in turn to the Duke of Lennox, the Duchess of Richmond and Lord Maltravers. It ceased by order of Parliament in 1644.

	Fair	F	VF	EF
JAMES I **Royal farthing tokens**				
Type 1 Harington (circa 1613). Small copper flan with tin-washed surface, mint-mark between sceptres below crown	£10	£35	£150	*
Type 2 Harington (circa 1613). Larger flan, no tin wash	£12	£25	£90	*
Type 3 Lennox (1614-25). IACO starts at 1 o'clock position	£8	£20	£60	*
Type 4 Lennox (1622-25). Oval flan, IACO starts at 7 o'clock	£12	£30	£90	*
CHARLES I **Royal farthing tokens**				
Type 1 Richmond (1625-34). Single arched crown	£8	£15	£40	*
Type 2 Transitional (circa 1634). Double arched crown	£8	£20	£60	*
Type 3 Maltravers (1634-36). Inner circles	£8	£20	£45	£95
Type 4 Richmond (1625-34). As Type 1 but oval	£8	£30	*	*
Type 5 Maltravers (1634-36). Double arched crown	£15	£50	*	*
Rose farthing tokens (rose on reverse)				
Type 1 Small thick flan	£7	£15	£35	*
Type 2 Same, but single arched crown	£7	£15	£40	*
Type 3 Same, but sceptres below crown	£15	£50	*	*

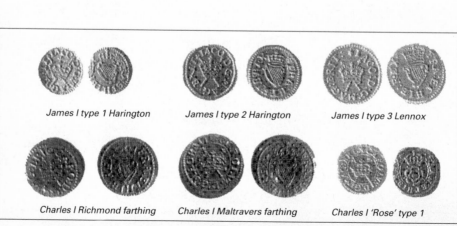

James I type 1 Harington	James I type 2 Harington	James I type 3 Lennox
Charles I Richmond farthing	Charles I Maltravers farthing	Charles I 'Rose' type 1

MILLED COINAGE from 1656

Again it must be stressed that the prices shown in this guide are the approximate amounts collectors can expect to pay for coins — they are not dealers' buying prices. Information for this guide is drawn from auction results and dealers' lists, with the aim of determining firm valuations. Prices still vary enormously from sale to sale and from one dealer's list to another. Allowance must also be made for the variance in the standards of grading. The prices given here aim at a reasonable assessment of the market at the time of compilation, but they are not the product of computers, which would, in any case, provide only average (not necessarily accurate) prices. It is not possible to forecast such values because of the erratic fluctuations that can occur, not only in boom conditions but also during times of economic uncertainty, and an annual catalogue of this type cannot be up to date on the bullion prices of common sovereigns, for example. If you are buying or selling bullion gold coins, refer to current quotations from bullion dealers.

With some denominations in the silver and copper series, column headings indicating condition change at the beginning of the lists of George III coins. The condition (grade) of a coin is of great importance in determining its market value. Notes on grading and on abbreviations etc. used in these price guides appear elsewhere in this publication.

Cromwell gold patterns

These were struck by order of Cromwell, with the consent of the Council. The dies were made by Thomas Simon, and the coins were struck on Peter Blondeau's machine. The fifty shillings and the broad were struck from the same dies, but the fifty shillings has the edge inscription PROTECTOR LITERIS LITERAE NUMMIS CORONA ET SALUS, while the broad is not so thick and has a grained edge. No original strikings of the half broad are known, but some were struck from dies made by John Tanner in 1738. All three denominations are dated 1656.

Cromwell half broad

	F	VF	EF	Unc
Fifty shillings	*	*£15000		*
Broad	*	£2000	£4000	£6000
Half broad	*	*	£4000	£7000

Five guineas

	F	VF	EF	Unc
CHARLES II				
1668-78 pointed end to trnctn of bust ...	£1000	£1750	£6500	*
1668, 69, 75 — eleph below bust ...	£1000	£1750	£6500	*
1675-8 — eleph & castle below bust ...	£1000	£1750	£6500	*
1678-84 rounded end to trnctn ...	£1000	£1650	£5000	*
1680-4 — eleph & castle	£1350	£1950	£7000	*
JAMES II				
1686 sceptres in wrong order on rev ...	£1000	£1750	£5000	£8500
1687-8 sceptres correct	£1000	£1750	£5000	*
1687-8 eleph & castle	£1000	£1950	£5500	*
WILLIAM AND MARY				
1691-4 no prov mark	£1100	£1950	£4750	£8500
1691-4 eleph & castle	£1250	£2000	£5500	*
WILLIAM III				
1699-1700 no prov mark	£900	£1650	£4000	*
1699 eleph & castle	£1000	£2000	£5000	*
1701 new bust 'fine work'	£1250	£2000	£4750	£7000

Charles II 1676 five guineas,
elephant and castle

George II 1729 five guineas

Charles II 1664 two guineas elephant below bust

James II 1687 two guineas

	F	VF	EF	Unc
ANNE				
Pre-Union with Scotland				
1703 VIGO below bust	*	*	£37500	*
1705-6 plain below	£1250	£1950	£5000	£8000
Post-Union with Scotland				
1706	£1150	£1750	£4500	£7500
1709 Larger lettering, wider shield and crowns	£1150	£1650	£4250	*
1711, 1713-4 broader bust	£1150	£1650	£4250	£6500

Pre-Union reverses have separate shields (top and right) for England and Scotland. Post-Union reverses have the English and Scottish arms side by side on the top and bottom shields.

	F	VF	EF	Unc
GEORGE I				
1716, 17, 20, 26	£1650	£2500	£7000	*
GEORGE II				
1729, 31, 35, 38, 41 YH	£1250	£1850	£3250	£6500
1729 E,I,C, below head	£1250	£1950	£3500	£7000
1746 OH, lima below	£1250	£2000	£4000	£7500
1748, 53 plain below	£1250	£2000	£3750	£7500
GEORGE III				
1770, 73, 77 patterns only	*	*	£40000	£50000

Two Guineas

	F	VF	EF	Unc
CHARLES II				
1664, 5, 9, 71 pointed end to trnctn	£600	£1100	£4000	*
1664 elephant below	£600	£1100	£3500	*
1675-84 rounded end to trnctn	£550	£800	£3000	*
1676, 78, 82-84 eleph & castle below bust	£700	£1350	£4500	*
1678 elephant below				ext. rare
JAMES II				
1687	£800	£1750	£4500	*
1688/9	£800	£1750	£5000	*
WILLIAM AND MARY				
1691, 3, 4 eleph & castle	£650	£1250	£3500	£5500
1693, 4 no prov mark	£600	£1000	£3000	*
WILLIAM III				
1701	£900	£1750	£3500	*
ANNE				
(none struck before Union)				
1709, 11, 13, 14	£500	£750	£1850	*
GEORGE I				
1717, 20, 26	£600	£900	£1850	£3250
GEORGE II				
1734, 5, 8, 9, YH (**F**)	£275	£450	£1100	£1950
1739, 40 intermediate head (**F**)	£250	£500	£1250	£2500
1748, 53 OH	£300	£550	£1450	£2750
GEORGE III				
1768, 73, 77 patterns only	*	*	£13500	£25000

Guineas

	F	VF	EF	Unc
CHARLES II				
1663 pointed trnctn	£400	£750	£3000	£6000
1663 — eleph	£400	£750	£3500	*
1664 trnctn indented	£400	£750	£3000	*
1664 — eleph	*	*	£6000	*

	F	VF	EF	Unc
1664-73 sloping pointed trnctn	£300	£600	£2750	£5500
1664, 5, 8 — eleph	£400	£1000	£3250	*
1672-84 rounded trnctn	£250	£500	£2500	*
1674-84 — eleph & castle	£400	£850	£4000	*
1677, 8 — eleph	*	£1750	*	*

JAMES II

	F	VF	EF	Unc
1685, 6 1st bust	£200	£475	£1750	£3000
1685 — eleph & castle	£225	£550	£1900	*
1686-8 2nd bust	£225	£525	£1750	£3000
1686-8 — eleph & castle	£225	£550	£1850	*

WILLIAM AND MARY

	F	VF	EF	Unc
1689-94 no prov mark	£275	£475	£1750	£3500
1689-94 eleph & castle	£300	£575	£2000	*
1692 eleph	£500	£1200	*	*

WILLIAM III

	F	VF	EF	Unc
1695, 6 1st bust	£200	£350	£1500	£2500
1695, 7 — eleph & castle	*	*	*	*
1697-1701 2nd bust	£200	£350	£1500	*
1698-1701 — eleph & castle	£450	£110	*	*
1701 3rd bust 'fine work'	£350	£600	£2500	*

Charles II 1663 guinea elephant below bust

ANNE

Pre-Union[1]

	F	VF	EF	Unc
1702, 1705-7 plain below bust	£275	£600	£1500	£2750
1703 VIGO below	£500	*	*	*

Post-Union[1]

	F	VF	EF	Unc
1707, 8 1st bust	£150	£250	£750	£1500
1707 — eleph & castle	£400	£850	£2750	*
1707-9 2nd bust	£150	£250	£750	£1500
1708, 9 — eleph & castle	£450	£1100	£3500	*
1710-1714 3rd bust	£150	£225	£700	£1250

[1]See note in prices of five guinea pieces for Anne.

GEORGE I

	F	VF	EF	Unc
1714 1st head PR. EL. (Prince Elector) in rev legend	£300	£600	£2000	£3000
1715 2nd head, tie with two ends ...	£150	£250	£750	£1850
1715 3rd head, hair not curling round trnctn	£175	£300	£1000	*
1716-23 4th head, tie with loop... ...	£150	£225	£750	£1750
1721, 2 — eleph & castle	*	*	*	*
1723-7 5th head, smaller, older bust	£175	£250	£1000	£2250
1726 — eleph & castle	£500	£1350	*	*

Anne 1706 guinea

GEORGE II

	F	VF	EF	Unc
1727 1st YH, small lettering	£300	£500	£1800	£2500
1727, 8 — larger lettering	£275	£400	£1800	*
1729-32 2nd YH (narrower)	£175	£300	£1500	*
1729, 31, 2 — E.I.C. below	£175	£375	£1700	£2250
1732-8 — larger lettering	£175	£250	£1350	£1750
1732 — — E.I.C. below	£300	£500	£1750	*
1739, 40, 43 intermediate head ...	£175	£275	£750	£1500
1739 — E.I.C. below	£300	£700	*	*
1745, 6 — larger lettering	£175	£350	£800	*
1745 — LIMA below	£350	£750	£2500	*
1747-53, 5, 6, 8, 9, 60, OH	£150	£250	£750	£1500

GEORGE III

	F	VF	EF	Unc
1761, 1st head	£325	£750	£2250	£3500
1763, 4, 2nd head	£195	£500	£1700	*
1765-73, 3rd head	£100	£175	£600	*
17749, 81-6, 4th head	£95	£165	£325	£650
1789-99, 5th head, 'spade' rev (F) ...	£90	£125	£250	£400
1813, 6th head, rev shield in Garter ('Military guinea')	£175	£350	£750	£1250

George III 1813 'Military guinea'

William and Mary 1691 half guinea

Half Guineas

CHARLES II	F	VF	EF	Unc
1669-72 bust with pointed trnctn	£175	£325	£1650	*
1672-84 rounded trnctn	£175	£325	£1650	*
1676-8, 80, 82-4 — eleph & castle	£250	£500	£2500	*

JAMES II				
1686-8 no prov mark	£150	£300	£1500	£2250
1686 eleph & castle	£600	*	*	*

WILLIAM AND MARY				
1689 1st busts	£200	£400	£1500	£2750
1690-4 2nd busts...	£200	£350	£1500	*
1691-2 — eleph & castle	£250	£400	£1750	*
1692 — eleph				ext. rare

WILLIAM III				
1695 no prov mark	£125	£200	£1000	£1750
1695, 6 eleph & castle...	£300	£650	£2000	*
1697-1701 larger harp on rev	£150	£225	£1200	*
1698 — eleph & castle	£275	£450	£2000	*

William III 1695 half guinea

ANNE				
Pre-Union 1				
1702, 5 plain below bust	£225	£450	£1500	*
1703 VIGO below...	£2500	£3500	*	*
Post Union[1]				
1707-14 plain	£100	£175	£550	£1250

[1]See note in prices of five guineas for Anne.

George I 1719 half guinea

GEORGE 1				
1715, 17-23, 1st head	£125	£200	£600	£1200
1721 eleph & castle	£300	£800	*	*
1724-7, smaller older head	£125	£200	£600	£1200

GEORGE II				
1728-39 YH...	£135	£235	£850	£1750
1729-32, 9 — E.I.C. below...	£165	£325	£1200	*
1740, 3, 5, 6, intermediate head	£150	£275	£750	*
1745 — LIMA below	£650	£1000	£2750	*
1747-53, 5, 6, 58-60 OH	£125	£150	£500	£800

George I half guinea, 1725

GEORGE III				
1762, 3, 1st head...	£200	£375	£1000	*
1764-6, 8, 9, 72-5, 2nd head	£100	£150	£400	£750
1774, 5, 3rd head...	£250	£600	£1500	*
1775-9, 81, 83-6, 4th head	£75	£100	£250	£450
1787-91, 93-8, 1800, 5th head ...	£60	£80	£175	£350
1801-3, 6th head	£60	£75	£165	£300
1804, 6, 8-11, 13, 7th head	£60	£75	£165	£300

George III 1786 half guinea

Third guineas

GEORGE III	F	VF	EF	Unc
1797-1800 1st head	£35	£55	£100	£195
1801-3 — date close to crown on reverse	£35	£55	£100	£195
1804, 6, 8-11, 13, 2nd head	£35	£65	£125	£200

George III 1788 half guinea with 'spade' type shield on reverse

Quarter guineas

GEORGE I	F	VF	EF	Unc
1718	£40	£75	£110	£195

GEORGE III	F	VF	EF	Unc
1762	£45	£75	£150	£250

George I 1718 quarter guinea

58

It should be noted that all coins less than 100 years old are subject to VAT at the current rate, in addition to the prices given here.

N.B. Forgeries exist of pieces marked (F) and if discovered should be reported to the police.

Brittannias
(See under Decimal Coinage)

Five pounds

	F	VF	EF	Unc
GEORGE III				
1820 pattern (F) ...	*	*	*	£50000
GEORGE IV				
1826 proof	*_	*	£5500	£8000
VICTORIA				
1839 proof with 'Una and the Lion' rev (F)	*	*	£12500	£17500
1887 JH (F)	£300	£425	£550	£700
1887 proof	*	*	£950	£1750
1893 OH (F)	£400	£550	£750	£1100
1893 proof	*	*	£1000	£2000
EDWARD VII				
1902 (F)	£325	£400	£475	£575
1902 proof	*	*	£500	£600
GEORGE V				
1911 proof (F)	*	*	*	£1100
GEORGE VI				
1937 proof	*	*	*	£600
ELIZABETH II				

In 1984 the Royal Mint issued the first of an annual issue of Brilliant Uncirculated £5 coins. These bear the symbol 'U' in a circle to the left of the date on the reverse to indicate the standard of striking.

1981 proof	£400
1984	£400
1985	£425
1986	£425
1987 new effigy	£425
1988 —	£425
1989 500th anniversary of the sovereign, BU	£450
1990 Queen Mother's 90th birthday, proof	£575
1990	£435
1991	£450
1992	£450
1993 Coronation, proof	£725
1993	£475
1994	£500
1995	£535
1996 Queens 70 Birthday, proof	£645
... ... BU	£575

Reverse of the gold proof five pounds marking the Queen Mother's 90th birthday (for silver and cupro-nickel versions see Decimal Coinage)

Two pounds

	F	VF	EF	Unc
GEORGE III				
1820 pattern (F)...	*	*	£9500	£12500

George III 1820 pattern two pounds

	F	VF	EF	Unc
GEORGE IV				
1823 St George on reverse (F)	£195	£325	£500	£1250
1826 proof, shield reverse ...	*	*	£1950	£2950

William IV 1831 proof two pounds

	F	VF	EF	Unc
WILLIAM IV				
1831 proof	*	*	£2500	£4250
VICTORIA				
1887 JH (F)	£165	£200	£240	£275
1887 proof	*	*	£450	£800
1893 OH (F)	£175	£250	£375	£495
1893 proof	*	*	£500	£900
EDWARD VII				
1902 (F)	£160	£195	£230	£275
1902 proof	*	*	£240	£295
GEORGE V				
1911 proof (F) ...	*	*	*	£500

1937 proof two pounds

	F	VF	EF	Unc
GEORGE VI				
1937 proof ...	*	*	*	£325

TWO POUNDS

	F	VF	EF	Unc
ELIZABETH II				
1983 proof				£200
1986 Commonwealth Games, proof				£200
1987 proof				£250
1988 proof				£250
1989 500th anniversary of the sovereign, proof				£300
1990 proof				£275
1991 proof				£275
1993 proof				£305
1994 gold proof				£425
1994 gold proof 'mule'				£600
1995 VE day gold proof				£400
1995 50th Anniversary of UN, proof ...				£300
1996 European Football Championship ...				£350

Sovereigns

GEORGE III	F	VF	EF	Unc
1817 (F)	£100	£175	£375	£600
1818	£100	£195	£450	£750
1819				ext. rare
1820	£100	£175	£400	£650

GEORGE IV
Type laureat head/St George

	F	VF	EF	Unc
1821	£100	£165	£375	£600
1822 (F)	£100	£165	£400	£650
1823	£130	£200	£650	*
1824	£100	£165	£375	£600
1825	£125	£350	£950	*

George IV 1826 proof sovereign

Type bare head/shield

	F	VF	EF	Unc
1825 (F)	£95	£150	£375	£650
1826	£95	£150	£395	£700
1826 proof	*	*	£800	£1750
1827 (F)	£95	£150	£395	£700
1828 (F)	£500	£1500	£3750	*
1829	£95	£150	£375	£650
1830	£95	£150	£375	£650

WILLIAM IV

	F	VF	EF	Unc
1831	£100	£165	£450	£750
1831 proof	*	*	£1000	£2500

William IV 1831 proof sovereign

	F	VF	EF	Unc
1832 (F)	£100	£165	£375	£600
1833	£100	£175	£395	£650
1835	£100	£165	£375	£600
1836	£100	£165	£375	£600
1837	£100	£165	£375	£650

VICTORIA
Type 1, YH obv, shield rev

	F	VF	EF	Unc
1838	£70	£90	£200	£550

Victoria 1839 proof sovereign

	F	VF	EF	Unc
1839	£95	£175	£750	£1200
1839 proof	*	*	£1000	£1950
1841	£400	£700	£2750	*
1842	*	*	£125	£400
1843	*	*	£125	£350
1843 narrow shield	£650	£1200	£2000	*
1844	*	*	£125	£300
1845	*	*	£125	£300
1846	*	*	£125	£300
1847	*	*	£125	£300
1848	*	*	£125	£300
1849	*	*	£125	£375
1850	*	*	£125	£250
1851	*	*	£125	£250
1852	*	*	£125	£250
1853	*	*	£110	£250

Victoria 1853 sovereign, shield on reverse

	F	VF	EF	Unc
1853 proof	*	*	*	£3000
1854	*	*	£100	£250
1855	*	*	£100	£250
1856	*	*	£100	£250
1857	*	*	£100	£250
1858	*	*	£300	£750
1859	*	*	£100	£200
1859 'Ansell'	£80	£200	£900	*
1860	*	*	£200	£600
1861	*	*	£95	£200
1862	*	*	£95	£200
1863	*	*	£80	£175
1863 die number below wreath on rev	*	*	£75	£175
1863 '827' on truncation ...	£1000	£1500	£2500	*
1864 die no. ...	*	*	£85	£175
1865 die no. ...	*	*	£85	£175
1866 die no. ...	*	*	£85	£175
1868 die no. ...	*	*	£85	£175
1869 die no. ...	*	*	£85	£175
1870 die no. ...	*	*	£85	£175
1871 die no. ...	*	*	£85	£125
1871 S (Sydney mint) below wreath	*	*	£85	£400
1872	*	*	£80	£150
1872 die no. ...	*	*	£70	£125
1872 M (Melbourne mint) below wreath	*	*	£120	£300
1872 S	*	*	£85	£350
1873 die no. ...	*	*	£80	£175
1873 S	*	*	£85	£325
1874 die no. ...	£250	£650	£2500	*
1874 M ...	*	*	£85	£325
1875 S	*	*	£85	£325
1877 S	*	*	£85	£300

	F	VF	EF	Unc
1878 S	*	*	£95	£300
1879 S	*	*	£95	£300
1880 M	£350	£1000	£2000	£3500
1880 S	*	*	£95	£300
1881 M	*	£100	£300	£500
1881 S	*	*	£95	£300
1882 M	*	*	£95	£300
1882 S	*	*	£95	£300
1883 M	*	£350	£800	£1500
1883 S	*	*	£95	£300
1884 M	*	*	£95	£300
1884 S	*	*	£90	£300
1885 M	*	*	£85	£250
1885 S	*	*	£85	£250
1886 M	£500	£1500	£3000	£4000
1886 S	*	*	£80	£250
1887 M	£300	£750	£1750	£2500
1887 S	*	*	£90	£250

Type II. YH obv, St George and Dragon rev

	F	VF	EF	Unc
1871	*	*	£75	£150
1871 S below head	*	£150	£500	£1250
1872	*	*	£75	£250
1872 M below head	*	£150	£500	*
1872 S	*	*	£400	*
1873	*	*	£75	£140
1873 M	*	£150	£650	£1500
1873 S	*	*	£350	*
1874	*	*	£75	£175
1874 M	*	*	£300	*
1874 S	*	*	£300	*
1875 M	*	*	£300	£850
1875 S	*	*	£250	*
1876	*	*	£75	*
1876 M	*	*	£350	*
1876 S	*	*	£350	*
1877 M	*	*	£300	£750
1878	*	*	£75	£150
1878 M	*	*	£250	£500
1879	£65	£150	£600	*
1879 M	*	*	£250	*
1879 S	*	*	£350	*
1880	*	*	£70	*
1880 M	*	*	£250	*
1880 S	*	*	£150	£350
1881 M	*	*	£200	*
1881 S	*	*	£150	£350
1882 M	*	*	£250	*
1882 S	*	*	£150	£350
1883 M	*	*	£350	£1500
1883 S	*	*	£150	£350
1884	*	*	£70	£150
1884 M	*	*	£200	£400
1884 S	*	*	£200	£400
1885	*	*	£70	£150
1885 M	*	*	£150	£350
1885 S	*	*	£150	£350
1886 M	*	*	£150	£350
1886 S	*	*	£150	£350
1887 M	*	*	£150	£350
1887 S	*	*	£150	£350

Jubilee head coinage

	F	VF	EF	Unc
1887 (F)	*	*	£60	£85
1887 proof	*	*	£300	£450
1887 M on ground below dragon	*	*	£100	£250
1887 S on ground below dragon	*	*	£275	£550
1888	*	*	*	£90
1888 M	*	*	*	£125
1888 S	*	*	*	£125
1889	*	*	*	£90
1889 M	*	*	*	£125

	F	VF	EF	Unc
1889 S	*	*	*	£100
1890	*	*	*	£85
1890 M	*	*	*	£100
1890 S	*	*	*	£100
1891	*	*	*	£85
1891 M	*	*	*	£100
1891 S	*	*	*	£100
1892	*	*	*	£85
1892 M	*	*	*	£100
1892 S	*	*	*	£100
1893 M	*	*	*	£100
1893 S	*	*	*	£100

Old head coinage

	F	VF	EF	Unc
1893	*	*	*	£85
1893 proof	*	*	£350	£500
1893 M	*	*	*	£85
1893 S	*	*	*	£95
1894	*	*	*	£80
1894 M	*	*	*	£85
1894 S	*	*	*	£95
1895	*	*	*	£80
1895 M	*	*	*	£85
1895 S	*	*	*	£95
1896	*	*	*	£80
1896 M	*	*	*	£85
1896 S	*	*	*	£95
1897 M	*	*	*	£85
1897 S	*	*	*	£95
1898	*	*	*	£80
1898 M	*	*	*	£95
1898 S	*	*	*	£100
1899	*	*	*	£80

1898 Victoria Old Head sovereign

	F	VF	EF	Unc
1899 M	*	*	*	£100
1899 P (Perth mint) on ground below dragon	*	*	*	£150
1899 S	*	*	*	£125
1900	*	*	*	£75
1900 M	*	*	*	£90
1900 P	*	*	*	£90
1900 S	*	*	*	£125
1901	*	*	*	£85
1901 M	*	*	*	£85
1901 P	*	*	*	£85
1901 S	*	*	*	£100

EDWARD VII

	F	VF	EF	Unc
1902	*	*	*	£75
1902 proof	*	*	£80	£125
1902 M	*	*	*	£75
1902 P	*	*	*	£75
1902 S	*	*	*	£75
1903	*	*	*	£75
1903 M	*	*	*	£75
1903 P	*	*	*	£75
1903 S	*	*	*	£75
1904	*	*	*	£75
1904 M	*	*	*	£75
1904 P	*	*	*	£75
1904 S	*	*	*	£75
1905	*	*	*	£75
1905 M	*	*	*	£75
1905 P	*	*	*	£75

SOVEREIGNS

		F	VF	EF	Unc
1905 S	... ...	*	*	*	£75
1906	... ...	*	*	*	£75
1906 M	... ...	*	*	*	£75
1906 P	... ...	*	*	*	£75
1906 S	... ...	*	*	*	£75
1907	... ...	*	*	*	£75
1907 M	... ...	*	*	*	£75
1907 P	... ...	*	*	*	£75
1907 S	... ...	*	*	*	£75
1908	... ...	*	*	*	£75
1908 C (Canada, Ottawa mint) on ground below dragon (F)		*	*	£1500	£2500
1908 M	... ...	*	*	*	£75
1908 P	... ...	*	*	*	£75
1908 S	... ...	*	*	*	£75
1909	... ...	*	*	*	£75
1909 C	... ...	*	*	£225	£500
1909 M	... ...	*	*	*	£75
1909 P	... ...	*	*	*	£75
1909 S	... ...	*	*	*	£75
1910	... ...	*	*	*	£75
1910 C	... ...	*	*	£175	£400
1910 M	... ...	*	*	*	£75
1910 P	... ...	*	*	*	£75
1910 S	... ...	*	*	*	£75
GEORGE V					
1911	... ...	*	*	*	£70
1911 proof	...	*	*	£150	£250
1911 C	... ...	*	*	*	£70
1911 M	... ...	*	*	*	£70
1911 P	... ...	*	*	*	£70
1911 S	... ...	*	*	*	£70
1912	... ...	*	*	*	£70
1912 M	... ...	*	*	*	£70
1912 P	... ...	*	*	*	£70
1912 S	... ...	*	*	*	£70
1913	... ...	*	*	*	£70
1913 C (F)	...	*	£175	£250	£400
1913 M	... ...	*	*	*	£70
1913 P	... ...	*	*	*	£70
1913 S	... ...	*	*	*	£70
1914	... ...	*	*	*	£70
1914 C	... ...	*	£100	£150	£200
1914 M	... ...	*	*	*	£70
1914 P	... ...	*	*	*	£70
1914 S	... ...	*	*	*	£70
1915	... ...	*	*	*	£70
1915 M	... ...	*	*	*	£70
1915 P	... ...	*	*	*	£70
1915 S	... ...	*	*	*	£70
1916	... ...	*	*	*	£70
1916 C	... ...	*	*	£8000	*
1916 M	... ...	*	*	*	£70
1916 P	... ...	*	*	*	£70
1916 S	... ...	*	*	*	£70
1917 (F)	...	*	£1750	£2500	*
1917 C	... ...	*	*	£65	£110
1917 M	... ...	*	*	*	£70
1917 P	... ...	*	*	*	£70
1917 S	... ...	*	*	*	£70
1918	... ...	*	*	£75	£125
1918 I (Indian mint, Bombay), on ground below dragon		*	*	*	£80
1918 M	... ...	*	*	*	£70
1918 P	... ...	*	*	*	£70
1918 S	... ...	*	*	*	£70
1919 C	... ...	*	*	£85	£150
1919 M	... ...	*	*	*	£70
1919 P	... ...	*	*	*	£70
1919 S	... ...	*	*	*	£70
1920 M	... ...	*	£2000	£4000	*

		F	VF	EF	Unc
1920 P	... ...	*	*	*	£70
1920 S	... ...			highest	rarity
1921 M	... ...	*	£2000	£4500	£6500
1921 P	... ...	*	*	*	£80
1921 S	... ...	*	£500	£1200	£1750
1922 M	... ...	*	£1750	£4000	£6500
1922 P	... ...	*	*	*	£80
1922 S	... ...	*	£3500	£7000	£12000
1923 M	... ...	*	*	*	£80
1923 S	... ...	*	£2000	£4500	£7500
1923 SA (South Africa, Pretorial Mint) on ground below dragon	...	*	£1250	£1750	£2500
1924 M	... ...	*	*	£75	£100
1924 P	... ...	*	*	*	£85
1924 S	... ...	*	£350	£600	£1000
1924 SA	... ...	*	*	£1500	£1750
1925	... ...	*	*	*	£80
1925 M	... ...	*	*	*	£80
1925 P	... ...	*	*	£90	£150
1925 S	... ...	*	*	*	£80
1925 SA	... ...	*	*	*	£75
1926 M	... ...	*	*	£75	£110
1926 P	... ...	*	*	£250	£350
1926 S	... ...	*	£5000	£12000	£17000
1926 SA	... ...	*	*	*	£70
1927 P	... ...	*	*	£125	£250
1927 SA	... ...	*	*	*	£70
1928 M	... ...	*	£800	£1750	£2500
1928 P	... ...	*	*	£85	£120
1928 SA	... ...	*	*	*	£70
1929 M	... ...	*	£400	£900	£1500
1929 P	... ...	*	*	*	£70
1929 SA	... ...	*	*	*	£70
1930 M	... ...	*	*	£90	£150
1930 P	... ...	*	*	*	£70
1930 SA	... ...	*	*	*	£70
1931 M	... ...	*	£100	£200	£350
1931 P	... ...	*	*	*	£70
1931 SA	... ...	*	*	*	£70
1932 SA	... ...	*	*	*	£70
GEORGE VI					
1937 proof only		*	*	*	£375
ELIZABETH II					
1957	... ...	*	*	*	£65
1958	... ...	*	*	*	£65
1959	... ...	*	*	*	£65
1962	... ...	*	*	*	£65
1963	... ...	*	*	*	£65
1964	... ...	*	*	*	£65
1965	... ...	*	*	*	£65
1966	... ...	*	*	*	£65
1967	... ...	*	*	*	£65
1968	... ...	*	*	*	£65
1974	... ...	*	*	*	£65
1976	... ...	*	*	*	£65
1978	... ...	*	*	*	£65
1979	... ...	*	*	*	£65
1979 proof	... ...	*	*	*	£95
1980	... ...	*	*	*	£65
1980 proof	... ...	*	*	*	£95
1981	... ...	*	*	*	£65
1981 proof	... ...	*	*	*	£95
1982	... ...	*	*	*	£65
1982 proof	... ...	*	*	*	£95
1983 proof	... ...	*	*	*	£100
1984 proof	... ...	*	*	*	£100
1985 proof	... ...	*	*	*	£105
1986 proof	... ...	*	*	*	£105
1987 proof	... ...	*	*	*	£105
1988 proof	... ...	*	*	*	£105
1989 500th anniversary of the sovereign, proof		*	*	*	£140

Spink are publishers and suppliers of Numismatic books.

A CATALOGUE OF NUMISMATIC BOOKS
IS AVAILABLE ON APPLICATION TO
THE BOOK DEPARTMENT

BY APPOINTMENT TO
HER MAJESTY THE QUEEN
SPINK & SON LTD LONDON

BY APPOINTMENT TO
H.R.H. THE DUKE OF EDINBURGH
MEDALLISTS
SPINK & SON LTD LONDON

BY APPOINTMENT TO
H.R.H. THE PRINCE OF WALES
MEDALLISTS
SPINK & SON LTD LONDON

SPINK

SPINK & SON LTD, 5, 6 & 7 KING STREET, ST JAMES'S, LONDON SW1Y 6QS. TEL: 0171-930 7888. FAX: 0171-839 4853. TELEX: 916711
English Paintings and Watercolours · Oriental, Asian and Islamic Art · Textiles · Medals · Coins · Bullion · Banknotes

SOVEREIGNS

	F	VF	EF	Unc
1990 proof	*	*	*	£150
1991 proof	*	*	*	£160
1992 proof	*	*	*	£160
1993 proof	*	*	*	£160
1994 proof	*	*	*	£160
1995 proof	*	*	*	£160
1996 proof	*	*	*	£155

Half Sovereigns

GEORGE III

	F	VF	EF	Unc
1817 ...	£60	£80	£150	£300
1818	£50	£90	£175	£400
1820	£55	£95	£175	£400

GEORGE IV
Laureate head/ornate shield, date on rev

	F	VF	EF	Unc
1821	£250	£450	£1000	£1750
1823 plain shield	£70	£100	£275	£525
1824—	£65	£95	£250	£500
1825—	£65	£95	£250	£500

Bare head, date on obv/shield, full legend rev

	F	VF	EF	Unc
1826	£65	£90	£250	£525
1827	£65	£90	£250	£565
1828	£65	£90	£275	£600

WILLIAM IV

	F	VF	EF	Unc
1834 reduced size	£80	£125	£400	£750
1835 normal size	£80	£125	£375	£650
1836—	£200	£500	£1750	£2500
1837—	£80	£100	£375	£650

Victoria 1839 proof half sovereign

VICTORIA
Young head/shield rev

	F	VF	EF	Unc
1838	*	£50	£165	£350
1839 proof only ...	*	*	*	£850
1841	*	£50	£155	£350
1842	*	£50	£165	£375
1843	*	£50	£165	£425
1844	*	£50	£165	£375
1845	*	£150	*	*
1846	*	£60	£175	£425
1847	*	£50	£165	£375
1848	*	£80	£185	£500
1849	*	£60	£175	£400
1850	£80	£150	£550	£950
1851	*	£50	£165	£400
1852	*	£50	£165	£350
1853	*	£50	£165	£375
1854	£125	£200	*	*
1855	*	£50	£165	£350
1856	*	£50	£165	£350
1857	*	£50	£150	£300
1858	*	£50	£150	£300
1859	*	£50	£150	£300
1860	*	£50	£150	£300
1861	*	£50	£175	£375
1862	£200	£375	£1500	*
1863	*	£50	£150	£325
1863 die no. ...	*	£50	£145	£275
1864 die no. ...	*	£50	£145	£250
1865 die no. ...	*	£50	£145	£275
1866 die no. ...	*	£50	£145	£275
1867 die no. ...	*	£50	£145	£275
1869 die no. ...	*	£50	£145	£275

	F	VF	EF	Unc
1870 die no. ...	*	£50	£145	£275
1871 die no. ...	*	£50	£125	£275
1871 S below shield	*	£175	£650	£1500
1872 die no. ...	*	£50	£125	£275
1872 S	*	£175	£650	£1500
1873 die no. ...	*	£50	£125	£275
1873 M below shield	*	£175	£650	£1500

Victoria 1874 half sovereign

	F	VF	EF	Unc
1874 die no. ...	*	*	£100	£275
1875 die no. ...	*	*	£100	£275
1875 S	*	*	£650	£1500
1876 die no. ...	*	*	£100	£250
1877 die no. ...	*	*	£90	£200
1877 M	£100	£200	£850	£1650
1878 die no. ...	*	*	£90	£200
1879 die no. ...	*	*	£90	£200
1879 S	£100	£200	£750	£1550
1880	*	*	£90	£200
1880 die no. ...	*	*	£90	£200
1880 S	£150	£250	£900	£2000
1881 S	£150	£250	£900	£2000
1881 M	£150	£300	£900	£2000
1882 S	£200	£650	£3500	£6500
1882 M	*	£175	£750	£1600
1883	*	*	£90	£175
1883 S	£80	£175	£650	£1500
1884	*	*	£90	£175
1884 M	£80	£175	£750	£1500
1885	*	*	£85	£175
1885 M	£150	£400	£1500	£3750
1886 S	£65	£150	£650	£1500
1886 M	£100	£250	£1000	£3250
1887 S	£80	£175	£900	£2500
1887 M	£125	£500	£2500	£4500

Jubilee head/shield rev

	F	VF	EF	Unc
1887	*	*	£60	£80
1887 proof	*	*	£200	£375
1887 M	*	£150	£350	£750
1887 S	*	£150	£400	*
1889 S	*	£150	£350	*
1890	*	*	£50	£80
1891	*	*	£50	£80
1891 S	*	*	£400	£750
1892	*	*	£50	£85
1893	*	*	£50	£85
1893 M	*	*	£450	£1000

Old head/St George reverse

	F	VF	EF	Unc
1893	*	*	£45	£60
1893 proof	*	*	£225	£450
1893 M	£750	*	*	*
1893 S	£60	£120	£300	£800
1894	*	*	£45	£60
1895	*	*	£45	£60
1896	*	*	£45	£60
1896 M	£70	£125	£450	£1000
1897	*	*	£40	£65
1897 S	*	£90	£250	£450
1898	*	*	£40	£65
1899	*	*	£40	£65
1899 M	£70	£125	£450	£1500
1899 P proof only ...	*	*	*	£6000
1900	*	*	£40	£60
1900 M	£70	£125	£450	£1500
1900 P	£300	£500	£1200	£2500
1900 S	*	£80	£350	£1000
1901	*	*	£40	£65

		F	VF	EF	Unc
1901 P proof only	...	*	*	*	£6000

1902 matt proof half sovereign

EDWARD VII
				F	VF	EF	Unc
1902	...	...	...	*	*	*	£55
1902 proof	...	...	...	*	*	£75	£100
1902 S	...	...	...	*	*	£150	£450
1903	...	...	...	*	*	*	£60
1903 S	...	...	...	*	*	£90	£250
1904	...	...	...	*	*	*	£55
1904 P	...	...	...	£100	£200	£700	£1200
1905	...	...	...	*	*	*	£58
1906	...	...	...	*	*	*	£55
1906 M	...	...	...	*	*	£90	£350
1906 S	...	...	...	*	*	£85	£225
1907	...	...	...	*	*	*	£55
1907 M	...	...	...	*	*	£80	£200
1908	...	...	...	*	*	*	£55
1908 M	...	...	...	*	*	£80	£200
1908 P	...	...	...	*	£100	£600	*
1908 S	...	...	...	*	*	£80	£200
1909	...	...	...	*	*	*	£48
1909 M	...	...	...	*	*	£80	£275
1909 P	...	...	...	£70	£150	£500	£1500
1910	...	...	...	*	*	*	£48
1910 S	...	...	...	*	*	£80	£250

GEORGE V
				F	VF	EF	Unc
1911	...	...	...	*	*	*	£45
1911 proof	...	...	...	*	*	£100	£200
1911 P	...	...	...	*	*	£40	£80
1911 S	...	...	...	*	*	*	£50
1912	...	...	...	*	*	*	£45
1912 S	...	...	...	*	*	£40	£50
1913	...	...	...	*	*	*	£40
1914	...	...	...	*	*	*	£40
1914 S	...	...	...	*	*	*	£50
1915	...	...	...	*	*	*	£40
1915 M	...	...	...	*	*	£40	£50
1915 P	...	...	...	*	*	£40	£65
1915 S	...	...	...	*	*	*	£40
1916 S	...	...	...	*	*	*	£40
1918 P	...	...	...	*	£200	£500	£800
1923 SA proof	...	...	*	*	*	£165
1925 SA	...	...	...	*	*	*	£40
1926 SA	...	...	...	*	*	*	£40

GEORGE VI
			F	VF	EF	Unc
1937 proof	...	...	*	*	*	£175

ELIZABETH II
				F	VF	EF	Unc
1980 proof	...	...	...	*	*	*	£55
1982	...	...	...	*	*	*	£38
1982 proof	...	...	...	*	*	*	£60
1983 proof	...	...	...	*	*	*	£60
1984 proof	...	...	...	*	*	*	£60
1985 proof	...	...	...	*	*	*	£65
1986 proof	...	...	...	*	*	*	£65
1987 proof	...	...	...	*	*	*	£65
1988 proof	...	...	...	*	*	*	£65
1989 500th anniversary of the sovereign, proof			*	*	*	£85
1990 proof	...	...	...	*	*	*	£80
1991 proof	...	...	...	*	*	*	£80
1992 proof	...	...	...	*	*	*	£90
1993 proof	...	...	...	*	*	*	£85
1994 proof	...	...	...	*	*	*	£85
1995 proof	...	...	...	*	*	*	£85
1996 proof	...	...	...	*	*	*	£85

Crowns

CROMWELL	F	VF	EF
1658	£650	£950	£1700
1658 Dutch copy	*	£1650	£2850
1658 Tanner's copy	*	£2000	£3500

CHARLES II			
1662 1st bust	£80	£275	£2500
1663 —	£90	£350	£2750
1664 2nd bust	£95	£350	£3500
1665 —	£250	£600	*
1666 —	£85	£350	£3500
1666 — eleph	£150	£450	£4000
1667 —	£75	£300	£2500
1668 —	£70	£300	£2000
1668/7 —	£100	£350	£3000
1669 —	£200	£650	*
1669/8 —	£200	£750	£4000
1670 —	£80	£300	£2250
1670/69 —	£120	£350	*
1671 —	£75	£350	£2500
1671 3rd bust	£75	£300	£2250
1672 —	£75	£300	£2200
1673 —	£75	£300	£2250
1673/2 —	£80	£275	£2250
1674 —	£3000	highest rarity	
1675 —	£250	*	*
1675/4 —	£250	*	*
1676 —	£60	£250	£1500
1677 —	£70	£250	£1500
1677/6 —	£70	£250	£1500
1678/7 —	£100	£400	*
1679 —	£65	£250	£1500
1679 4th bust	£90	£250	£1500
1680 3rd bust	£100	£375	£2000
1680/79 —	£70	£250	£1750
1680 4th bust	£70	£250	£2000
1680/79 —	£110	£300	£2250
1681 — elephant & castle ...	£750	£2250	*
1681 —	£75	£300	£2250
1682 —	£100	£300	£2250
1682/1 —	£70	£300	£2250
1683 —	£150	£375	£2750
1684 —	£95	£350	£2250

JAMES II			
1686 1st bust	£75	£300	£1250
1687 2nd bust	£70	£120	£750
1688 —	£70	£125	£700
1688/7 —	£80	£150	£750

WILLIAM AND MARY			
1691	£150	£400	£1200
1692	£150	£350	£1000
1692/2 inverted QVINTO ...	£150	£350	£1000
1692/2 inverted QVARTO ...	£300	£750	*

WILLIAM III			
1695 1st bust	£50	£125	£425
1696 —	£50	£125	£425
1696 — GEI error	£125	£300	*
1696/5 —	£100	£200	£550
1696 2nd bust	*	*	*
1696 3rd bust	£50	£125	£450
1697	£300	£900	*
1700 3rd bust variety	£50	£125	£450

ANNE			
1703 1st bust VIGO ...	£175	£450	£2000
1705 —	£400	£800	£2500
1706 —	£125	£325	£800
1707 —	£100	£250	£700
1702 2nd bust	£85	£200	£600
1707 — E	£85	£200	£600
1708 —	£85	£225	£600

	F	VF	EF
1708 — E	£80	£225	*
1708/7 —	£90	£250	*
1708 — plumes	£110	£225	£600
1713 3rd bust	£110	£225	£600

GEORGE I			
1716	£150	£275	£1400
1718	£300	£500	£2000
1718/6	£200	£350	£1250
1720	£200	£350	£1250
1720/18	£150	£275	£1300
1723 SS C	£150	£300	£1250
1726 roses & plumes ...	£200	£400	£1850

GEORGE II			
1732 YH	£125	£250	£750
1732 — proof	*	*	£2000
1734	£125	£250	£750
1735	£125	£250	£650
1736	£125	£250	£650
1739	£125	£200	£625
1741	£125	£200	£600
1743 OH	£110	£195	£500

1739 Young Head Crown

1746 — LIMA	£110	£195	£500
1746 — proof	*	*	£1250
1750	£150	£250	£700
1751	£195	£300	£850

GEORGE III	F	VF	EF	Unc
Oval counter-stamp[1]	£75	£125	£250	£400
Octagonal Counterstamp[1] ...	£200	£350	£650	£950
1804 Bank of England dollar[1] ...	£50	£80	£225	£375
1818 LVIII	£10	£45	£200	£400
1818 — error edge ...	£250	*	*	*
1818 LIX	£10	£45	£175	£350

	F	VF	EF	Unc
1819 —	£10	£45	£200	£400
1819 — no edge stops	£50	£100	£350	*
1819/8 LIX	*	£100	£350	*
1819 LX	£10	£25	£200	£400
1819 — no stop after TUTAMEN ...	£30	£50	£275	*
1820 lx	*	*	£200	£400
1820/19	£50	£150	£300	*

[1]Beware of contemporary forgeries. The counterstamps are usually on Spanish-American dollars.

GEORGE IV

	F	VF	EF	Unc
1821 1st hd SEC ...	*	*	£225	£800
1821 — prf	*	*	*	£1500
1821 — TER error edge	*	*	£1500	£2500
1822 — SEC	*	*	£250	£900
1822 — — prf	*	*	*	*
1822 — TER	*	*	£275	£900
1822 — — prf	*	*	*	£2500
1823 — prf				£11000
1826 2nd hd prf ...	*	*	£1250	£2250

WILLIAM IV

	F	VF	EF	Unc
1831 w.w.	*	*	£3000	£4750
1831 w.WYON	*	*	£4000	£6500
1834 w.w.	*	*	*	£8500

VICTORIA

	F	VF	EF	Unc
1839 proof	*	*	£1250	£2750
1844 star stops	£20	£75	£600	£1500
1844 — prf	*	*	*	£5500
1844 cinquefoil stops	£20	£75	£600	£1500
1845	£20	£75	£600	£1500
1845 proof	*	*	*	£5000
1847	£20	£75	£700	£1750

Victoria 1847 Gothic crown

CROWNS

	F	VF	EF	Unc
1847 Gothic	£175	£300	£500	£1400
1847 — plain edge ...	*	£400	£750	£1750
1853 SEPTIMO	*	*	£2500	£4000
1853 plain	*	*	£3000	£5000
1887 JH	£10	£15	£25	£65
1887 — proof	*	*	£150	£350
1888 close date ...	£15	£25	£50	£85
1888 wide date	£10	£25	£75	£125
1889	£10	£15	£35	£75
1890	£10	£15	£35	£80
1891	£10	£15	£50	£100
1892	£10	£15	£50	£100
1893 LVI	£10	£15	£95	£150
1893 — proof	*	*	£150	£350
1893 LVII	£10	£40	£140	£275
1894 LVII	£10	£15	£95	£165
1894 LVIII	£10	£15	£95	£160
1895 LVIII	£10	£15	£95	£160
1895 LIX	£10	£15	£90	£140
1896 LIX	£10	£25	£175	£300
1896 LX	£10	£15	£90	£160
1897 LX	£10	£15	£90	£160
1897 LXI	£10	£15	£90	£160
1898 LXI	£10	£15	£125	£250
1898 LXII	£10	£15	£100	£185
1899 LXII	£10	£15	£85	£160
1899 LXIII	£10	£15	£95	£165
1900 LXIII	£10	£15	£95	£165
1900 LXIV	£10	£15	£95	£165

EDWARD VII

	F	VF	EF	Unc
1902	£15	£30	£65	£100
1902 matt proof ...	*	*	£75	£100

GEORGE V

	F	VF	EF	Unc
1927 proof	*	*	£75	£125
1928	£40	£65	£100	£150
1929	£40	£70	£100	£175
1930	£40	£65	£110	£175
1931	£40	£65	£110	£175
1932	£60	£95	£185	£300
1933	£40	£65	£110	£175
1934	£200	£350	£600	£850
1935	£4	£5	£8	£12
1935 rsd edge prf ...	*	*	£125	£200
1935 gold proof ...	*	*		*£10000
1935 prf in good silver (.925)	*	*	£650	£1250
1935 specimen	*	*	*	£40
1936	£40	£75	£165	£225

GEORGE VI

	F	VF	EF	Unc
1937	*	*	£8	£15
1937 proof	*	*	*	£25
1937 'VIP' proof ...	*	*	*	£500
1951	*	*	*	£4
1951 'VIP' proof ...	*	*	*	£300

ELIZABETH II

	F	VF	EF	Unc
1953	*	*	*	£7
1953 proof	*	*	*	£15
1953 'VIP' proof ...	*	*	*	£200
1960	*	*	*	£7
1960 'VIP' proof ...	*	*	*	£350
1960 polished dies ...	*	*	£4	£10
1965 Churchill	*	*	*	£1.50
1965 — 'satin' finish	*	*	*	£450

For issues 1972 onwards see under 25 pence in Decimal Coinage section.

Double florins

Victoria 1887 halfcrown

VICTORIA	F	VF	EF	Unc
1887 Roman 1 ...	*	£8	£15	£35
1887 — proof	*	*	£125	£225
1887 Arabic 1 ...	*	£10	£18	£45
1887 — proof	*	*	£90	£175
1888 ...	*	£10	£28	£75
1888 inverted 1 ...	£6	£20	£65	£150
1889	*	£8	£25	£60
1889 inverted 1 ...	£7	£25	£65	£150
1890	*	£10	£25	£70

Three shilling bank tokens

Contemporary forgeries of these pieces, as well as of other George III coins, were produced in quite large numbers. Several varieties exist for the pieces dated 1911 and 1812. Prices given here are for the commonest types of these years.

GEORGE III	F	VF	EF	Unc
1811	*	£10	£40	£75
1812 draped bust ...	*	£10	£40	£75
1812 laureate head ...	*	£10	£40	£75
1813	*	£10	£40	£75
1814	*	£10	£40	£75
1815	*	£10	£40	£75
1816	£70	£150	£300	£750

Halfcrowns

Cromwell 1658 halfcrown

CROMWELL			F	VF	EF
1656			£350	£850	£2500
1658			£350	£600	£1000

CHARLES II			F	VF	EF
1663 1st bust			£70	£350	£1500
1664 2nd bust			£85	£200	£1650
1666/3 3rd bust			£750	*	*
1666/3 — elephant			£200	£750	£4500
1667/4 —			*	*	*
1668/4 —			£125	£275	*
1669 —			£225	£600	*
1669/4 —			£125	£375	*
1670 —			£40	£150	£1000
1671 3rd bust var			£40	£150	£1000
1671/0 —			£60	£150	£1100
1672 —			£65	£160	£1100
1672 4th bust			£90	£250	£1200
1673 —			£40	£150	£1250
1673 — plume below ...			£1000	*	*
1673 — plume both sides			£1750	*	*
1674 —			£95	£350	*
1674/3 —			£110	*	*
1675 —			£40	£125	£750

Charles II 1676 halfcrown

			F	VF	EF
1676 —			£40	£125	£750
1677 —			£40	£125	£750
1678 —			£110	£300	*
1679 —			£40	£95	£750
1680 —			£125	£250	*
1681 —			£50	£150	£1000
1681/0 —			£50	£150	£1000
1681 — eleph & castle			£1250	*	*
1682 —			£100	£250	*
1682/1 —			£125	*	*
1682/79 —			£125	*	*
1683 —			£45	£110	£1250
1683 — plume below			£3000	*	*
1684/3 —			£150	*	*

James II 1687 halfcrown

JAMES II			F	VF	EF
1685 1st bust			£65	£185	£750
1686 —			£65	£185	£750
1686/5 —			£125	£350	*
1687 —			£65	£185	£750

	F	VF	EF
1687/6 —	£85	£225	£850
1687 2nd bust	£100	£295	£950
1688 —	£65	£185	£750

WILLIAM AND MARY

	F	VF	EF
1689 1st busts 1st shield ...	£60	£150	£500
1689 — 2nd shield ...	£60	£150	£500
1690 ——	£75	£175	£600
1691 2nd busts 3rd shield ...	£65	£175	£550
1692 ——	£65	£175	£550
1693 ——	£60	£150	£500
1693 —— 3 inverted	£85	£200	£750
1693 3 over 3 inverted ...	£80	£175	£600

William and Mary 1693 Halfcrown

WILLIAM III

	F	VF	EF
1696 large shield early harp	£15	£40	£140
1696 —— B...	£25	£80	£275
1696 —— C...	£30	£80	£275
1696 —— E...	£35	£90	£325
1696 —— N...	£30	£85	£350
1696 —— Y...	£25	£80	£325
1696 —— y/E	£60	*	*
1696 — ord harp...	£70	*	*
1696 —— C...	£70	*	*
1696 —— E	£80	£200	*
1696 —— N	£80	*	*
1696 small shield	£15	£45	£150
1696 — B	£25	£80	£300
1696 — C	£50	£125	*
1696 — E	£80	*	*
1696 — N	£25	£80	£300
1696 — y	£35	£90	£300
1696 2nd bust	*	*	*
1697 1st bust large shield ...	£15	£45	£125
1697 —— B	£25	£75	£200
1697 —— C	£30	£70	£250
1697 —— E	£30	£70	£250
1697 —— E/C	£75	£150	*
1697 —— N	£25	£70	£300
1697 —— y	£25	£70	£250

1697 Halfcrown of NORWICH: N below bust

	F	VF	EF
1698 ——	£15	£35	£150
1699 ——	£30	£100	£325

HALFCROWNS

	F	VF	EF
1700 ——	£15	£35	£150
1701 ——	£25	£45	£175
1701 — eleph & castle ...	£500	*	*
1701 — plumes	£100	£300	£750

ANNE

	F	VF	EF
1703 plain	£300	£700	£1600
1703 VIGO	£45	£125	£350
1704 plumes	£100	£200	£650
1705 —	£65	£165	£500
1706 r & p	£35	£100	£225
1707 —	£30	£100	£225
1707 plain	£35	£45	£125
1707 E	£30	£75	£225
1708 plain	£20	£45	£120
1708 E	£30	£75	1300
1708 plumes	£40	£125	£300
1709 plain	£25	£60	£125
1709 E	£150	*	*
1710 r & p	£40	£125	£250
1712 —	£35	£85	£200
1713 plain	£50	£175	£500
1713 r & p	£30	£85	£250
1714 —	£30	£85	£275
1714/3	£85	*	*

GEORGE I

	F	VF	EF
1715 proof	*	*	£2500
1715 r & p	£80	£175	£600
1717 —	£95	£275	£700
1720 —	£125	£300	£800
1720/17 —	£75	£165	£575
1723 SS C	£65	£140	£400
1726 small r & p	£1000		*

Spanish Half Dollar with George III counterstamp
(octagonal)

GEORGE II

	F	VF	EF
1731 YH proof	*	*	£1800
1731	£50	£140	£400
1732	£50	£140	£400
1734	£50	£140	£400
1735	£50	£140	£425
1736	£50	£140	£400
1739	£40	£110	£275
1741	£80	£175	£450
1743 OH	£40	£65	£200
1745	£40	£55	£150
1745 LIMA	£35	£70	£175
1746 —	£35	£70	£175
1746 plain, proof	*	*	£750
1750	£70	£175	£350
1751	£85	£185	£400
1741/39	£50	£100	£250

GEORGE III	F	VF	EF	Unc
Oval counterstamp usually on Spanish half dollar	£85	£175	£325	*

HALFCROWNS

	F	VF	EF	Unc
1816 large head ...	*	£40	£100	£200
1817 —	*	£40	£100	£200
1817 small head ...	*	£40	£100	£185
1818	*	£40	£100	£200
1819	*	£40	£100	£200
1819/8	*	*	*	*
1820	*	£45	£125	£225

George IV halfcrown of 1821

GEORGE IV

	F	VF	EF	Unc
1820 1st hd 1st rev ...	*	£40	£125	£250
1821 — ...	*	£45	£125	£250
1821 proof	*	*	£450	£750
1823	£300	£750	£2250	*
1823 — 2nd rev ...	*	£45	£125	£275
1824 — — ...	£25	£50	£175	£375
1824 2nd hd 3rd rev	£1000	*	*	*
1825 — —	*	£25	£90	£200
1826 — —	*	£20	£90	£200
1826 — — proof ...	*	*	£200	£450
1828 — —	*	£28	£175	£300
1829 — —	*	£28	£125	£250

William IV 1831 halfcrown

WILLIAM IV

	F	VF	EF	Unc
1831	*	*	*	*
1831 proof	*	*	£250	£475
1834 ww	£15	£30	£100	£250
1834 *ww* in script ...	£8	£15	£100	£200
1835	£5	£20	£125	£250
1836	£5	£15	£100	£200
1836/5	£25	£60	£195	*
1837	£5	£20	£125	£300

VICTORIA

From time to time halfcrowns bearing dates ranging from 1861 to 1871 are found, but except for rare proofs: 1853, 1862, and 1864, no halfcrowns were struck between 1850 and 1874, so pieces dated for this period are now considered to be contemporary or later forgeries.

	F	VF	EF	Unc
1839 plain and ornate fillets, ww	*	£550	£1750	*
1839 — plain edge proof	*	*	£325	£650
1839 plain fillets, ww incuse	*	£600	£1750	£2500
1840	£7	£25	£120	£225
1841	£75	£225	£700	£1000
1842	£6	£18	£110	£250
1843	£35	£80	£250	£475
1844	£6	£18	£125	£250
1845	£6	£18	£175	£300
1846	£9	£20	£175	£300
1848	£75	£175	£450	£850
1848/6	£75	£200	£550	£950
1849 large date ...	£15	£50	£200	£450
1849 small date ...	£50	£175	£375	£750
1850	£15	£50	£225	£425
1853 proof	*	£350	£600	£1000
1862 proof	*	*	£1500	£2250
1864 proof	*	*	£1500	£2250
1874	*	£20	£95	£150
1875	*	£12	£70	£140
1876	*	£28	£120	£200
1876/5	*	*	*	*
1877	*	£12	£70	£140
1878	*	£12	£70	£140
1879	*	£15	£85	£120
1880	*	£10	£65	£120
1881	*	£10	£60	£100
1882	*	£10	£60	£120
1883	*	£10	£60	£95
1884	*	£10	£60	£95
1885	*	£10	£60	£95
1886	*	£10	£60	£95
1887 YH	*	£12	£70	£120
1887 JH	*	£5	£15	£35
1887 — proof	*	*	£70	£130
1888	*	£6	£25	£50
1889	*	£5	£25	£45
1890	*	£6	£30	£55
1891	*	£6	£30	£65
1892	*	£6	£30	£65
1893 OH	*	£6	£35	£60
1893 — proof	*	*	£80	£150
1894	*	£6	£35	£60
1895	*	£6	£35	£60
1896	*	£6	£35	£60
1897	*	£6	£35	£60
1898	*	£6	£35	£60
1899	*	£6	£35	£65
1900	*	£6	£35	£60
1901	*	£6	£30	£60

EDWARD VII

	F	VF	EF	Unc
1902	*	£6	£20	£35
1902 matt proof ...	*	*	*	£40
1903	£20	£65	£300	£600
1904	£15	£45	£185	£425
1905 (F)	£65	£200	£900	£1500
1906	*	£20	£85	£175
1907	*	£25	£85	£200
1908	*	£20	£175	£275
1909	*	£8	£85	£175
1910	*	£6	£35	£70

GEORGE V

	F	VF	EF	Unc
1911	*	£4	£30	£65
1911 proof	*	*	*	£85
1912	£1.20	£3	£35	£80
1913	£1.20	£3	£40	£90
1914	*	*	£10	£30
1915	*	*	£10	£20
1916	*	*	£10	£20

	F	VF	EF	Unc
1917	*	£2	£10	£28
1918	*	*	£10	£20
1919	*	*	£12	£20
1920	*	*	£15	£40
1921	*	*	£17	£40
1922	*	*	£17	£50
1923	*	*	£10	£20
1924	*	*	£10	£30
1925	£3	£12	£140	£200

George V 1926 halfcrown

1926	*	*	£25	£65
1926 mod eff	*	*	£35	£85
1927	*	*	£12	£40
1927 new rev, proof	*	*	*	£25
1928	*	*	£4	£25
1929	*	*	£4	£20
1930	£3	£12	£95	£175
1931	*	*	£4	£20
1932	*	*	£15	£35
1933	*	*	£4	£20
1934	*	*	£17	£35
1935	*	*	£3	£12
1936	*	*	£2	£10

GEORGE VI

1937	*	*	*	£9
1937 proof	*	*	*	£12
1938	*	*	£4	£20
1939	*	*	*	£14
1940	*	*	*	£8
1941	*	*	*	£7
1942	*	*	*	£7
1943	*	*	*	£7
1944	*	*	*	£7
1945	*	*	*	£7
1946	*	*	*	£4
1947	*	*	*	£4
1948	*	*	*	£4
1949	*	*	*	£8
1950	*	*	*	£8
1950 proof	*	*	*	£10
1951	*	*	*	£8
1951 proof	*	*	*	£10

ELIZABETH II

1953	*	*	*	£2
1953 proof	*	*	*	£8
1954	*	*	£3	£20
1955	*	*	*	£4
1956	*	*	*	£4
1957	*	*	*	£3
1958	*	*	£2.50	£15
1959	*	*	£4	£35
1960	*	*	*	£3
1961	*	*	*	£1
1962	*	*	*	£1
1963	*	*	*	£1
1964	*	*	*	*
1965	*	*	*	*
1966	*	*	*	*
1967	*	*	*	*

Florins

The first florins produced in the reign of Victoria bore the legend VICTORIA REGINA and the date, omitting DEI GRATIA (By the Grace of God). They are therefore known as 'Godless' florins.

The date of a Victorian Gothic florin is shown in Roman numerals, in Gothic lettering on the obverse for example: mdccclvii (1857). Gothic florins were issued during the period 1851–1887.

VICTORIA	F	VF	EF	Unc
1848 'Godless' proof with milled edge ...	*	*	*	£1000

Victoria 1849 'Godless' florin

	F	VF	EF	Unc
1849 — ww obliterated by circle	£5	£20	£50	£110
1849 — ww inside circle	£4	£18	£50	£110
1851 proof only ...	*	*	*	£4000
1852	£4	£30	£65	£125
1853	£4	£35	£65	£130
1853 no stop after date	£5	£30	£70	£135
1853 proof	*	*	*	£750
1854	£250	£500	£800	*
1855	£4	£30	£70	£130
1856	£5	£35	£125	£240
1857	£4	£28	£125	£130
1858	£4	£28	£125	£130
1859	£4	£28	£125	£130
1859 no stop after date	£6	£30	£125	£150
1860	£7	£40	£130	£185
1862	£15	£75	£200	£300
1863	£35	£125	£300	£600
1864	£4	£28	£125	£190
1865	£5	£30	£125	£180
1865 colon after date	£6	£40	£125	£180
1866	£5	£30	£125	£185
1866 colon after date	£6	£30	£140	£200
1867	£8	£40	£150	£200
1868	£5	£30	£140	£190
1869	£4	£30	£125	£200
1870	£4	£30	£135	£185
1871	£4	£30	£125	£185

Victoria 1871 Gothic florin

FLORINS

	F	VF	EF	Unc
1872	£4	£26	£70	£125
1873	£4	£30	£70	£125
1874	£4	£28	£70	£125
1874 xxiv-/iii (die 29)	£50	£95	*	*
1875	£5	£30	£70	£125
1876	£5	£30	£70	£125
1877	£5	£30	£75	£140
1877 no ww	£25	*	*	*
1877 42 arcs	£25	*	*	*
1878	£4	£28	£70	£125
1879 ww 48 arcs ...	£6	£28	£75	£130
1879 die no.	£8	£40	£125	£225
1879 ww, 42 arcs ...	£10	£40	£70	£130
1879 no ww, 38 arcs	£5	£28	£70	£120
1880	£4	£26	£65	£110
1881	£4	£26	£65	£110
1881 xxri	£6	£28	£70	£120
1883	£4	£26	£65	£110
1884	£4	£26	£65	£110
1885	£4	£26	£65	£110
1886	£4	£28	£65	£110
1887 33 arcs	£6	£30	£70	£130
1887 46 arcs	£6	£40	£130	£175
1887 JH	£4	£5	£12	£20
1887 — proof	*	*	£45	£90
1888	*	£5	£25	£40
1889	*	£5	£25	£40
1890	£5	£15	£40	£80
1891	£15	£40	£110	£195
1892	£15	£50	£100	£165
1893 OH	£2	£4	£24	£50
1893 proof	*	*	*	£110
1894	*	£5	£25	£50
1895	*	£5	£25	£50
1896	*	£5	£25	£50
1897	*	£5	£25	£50
1898	*	£4	£25	£50
1899	*	£4	£25	£50
1900	*	£3	£25	£50
1901	*	£3	£25	£50

Edward VII 1902 florin

EDWARD VII

	F	VF	EF	Unc
1902	*	£5	£18	£30
1902 matt proof ...	*	*	*	£35
1903	£3	£25	£40	£75
1904	£5	£32	£100	£195
1905	£7	£40	£250	£500
1906	*	£16	£30	£70
1907	*	£16	£40	£90
1908	£2	£18	£60	£135
1909	£3	£24	£70	£150
1910	*	£6	£20	£45

GEORGE V

	F	VF	EF	Unc
1911	*	£2.25	£25	£45
1911 proof	*	*	*	£50
1912	*	*	£30	£65

	F	VF	EF	Unc
1913	*	*	£35	£70
1914	*	*	£10	£25
1915	*	*	£8	£18
1916	*	*	£8	£18
1917	*	*	£8	£18
1918	*	*	£8	£15
1919	*	*	£8	£20
1920	*	*	£12	£35
1921	*	*	£10	£28
1922	*	*	£12	£32
1923	*	*	£12	£22
1924	*	*	£12	£35
1925	*	£35	£125	£200
1926	*	*	£25	£60
1927 proof only ...	*	*	*	£30

George V 1928 florin

	F	VF	EF	Unc
1928	*	*	£5	£12
1929	*	*	£5	£12
1930	*	*	£8	£50
1931	*	*	£4	£20
1932	*	£20	£90	£150
1933	*	*	£6	£15
1935	*	*	£6	£15
1936	*	*	£2	£8

GEORGE VI

	F	VF	EF	Unc
1937	*	*	£1	£7
1937 proof	*	*	*	£12
1938	*	*	£2	£15
1939	*	*	£1	£6
1940	*	*	£1	£6
1941	*	*	£1	£4
1942	*	*	*	£5
1943	*	*	*	£4
1944	*	*	*	£4
1945	*	*	*	£4
1946	*	*	*	£4
1947	*	*	*	£4
1948	*	*	*	£3
1949	*	*	*	£5
1950	*	*	*	£6
1950 proof	*	*	*	£8
1951	*	*	*	£5
1951 proof	*	*	*	£9

Elizabeth II 1956 florin

ELIZABETH II	F	VF	EF	Unc
1953	*	*	*	£2
1953 proof	*	*	*	£5
1954	*	*	*	£15
1955	*	*	*	£3
1956	*	*	*	£3
1957	*	*	*	£15
1958	*	*	*	£10
1959	*	*	*	£15
1960	*	*	*	£1
1961	*	*	*	£1
1962	*	*	*	*
1963	*	*	*	*
1964	*	*	*	*
1965	*	*	*	*
1966	*	*	*	*
1967	*	*	*	*

One and sixpence bank tokens

GEORGE III	F	VF	EF	Unc
1811	£4	£10	£28	£50
1812 laureat bust ...	£4	£10	£32	£60
1812 laureat head ...	£4	£10	£30	£60
1813	£4	£10	£32	£60
1814	£4	£10	£32	£60
1815	£4	£10	£32	£60
1816	£4	£10	£32	£60

Shillings

1658 shilling of Cromwell

CROMWELL	F	VF	EF
1658	£250	£400	£650
1658 Dutch copy	*	*	*

Charles II 1671 shilling, plumes below bust

CHARLES II			
1663 1st bust	£30	£90	£350
1663 1st bust var	£30	£90	£350
1666 —	*	*	*
1666 — eleph	£125	£400	£1500
1666 guinea hd, eleph	£450	£1000	*

	F	VF	EF
1666 2nd bust	£450	*	*
1668 1st bust var	£200	*	*
1668 2nd bust	£30	£90	£350
1668/7 —	£45	£110	£425
1669/6 1st bust var	£375	*	*
1669 2nd bust	*	*	*
1670 —	£45	£110	£425
1671 —	£55	£125	£475
1671 — plumes both sides	£150	£375	£950
1672 —	£35	£90	£350
1673 —	£40	£100	£450
1673/2 —	£50	£90	£425
1673 — plumes both sides	£175	£425	*
1674 —	£40	£100	£425
1674/3 —	£45	£150	£400
1674 — plumes both sides	£125	£400	£1000
1674 — plumes rev only ...	£135	£400	*
1674 3rd bust	£250	*	*
1675 —	£300	£650	*
1675/3 —	£300	£650	*
1675 2nd bust	£200	£500	*
1675/4 —	£200	£500	*
1675 — plumes both sides	£200	£450	*
1676 —	£25	£90	£350
1676/5 —	£30	£125	£400
1676 — plumes both sides	£175	£450	£1200
1677 —	£30	£90	£400
1677 — plume obv only ...	£300	*	*
1678 —	£45	£110	£425
1678/7 —	£45	£125	£450
1679 —	£30	£90	£325
1679/7 —	£45	£125	£425
1679 — plumes	£250	*	*
1679 — plumes obv only	£200	*	*
1680 —	£500	*	*
1680 — plumes	£175	£450	£1200
1680/79 —	*	*	*
1681 —	£95	£275	*
1681/0 —	£95	£275	*
1681/0 — eleph & castle ...	£850	*	*
1682/1 —	£175	*	*
1683 —	*	*	*
1683 4th bust	£75	£150	£575
1684 —	£45	£125	£500

James II 1685 shilling

JAMES II			
1685	£60	£175	£500
1685 no stops on rev	£125	*	*
1685 plume on rev	£2000	*	£7500
1686	£45	£125	£450
1686 V/S	£60	£150	£450
1687	£45	£125	£450
1687/6	£35	£100	£425
1688	£40	£115	£450
1688/7	£55	£125	£475

WILLIAM AND MARY			
1692	£50	£150	£425
1693	£45	£125	£400

SHILLINGS

WILLIAM III

	F	VF	EF
1695	£12	£35	£100
1696	£10	£20	£75
1696 no stops on rev	£12	£65	£165
1669 in error	£400	*	*
1696 1st bust B	£12	£40	£135
1696 — C	£12	£40	£135
1696 — E	£12	£40	£135
1696 — N	£12	£40	£135
1696 — Y	£12	£40	£135
1696 — Y	£15	£60	£175
1696 2nd bust		highest rarity	
1696 3rd bust C	£50	£150	£375
1696 — E	£125	*	*
1697 1st bust	£8	£20	£65
1697 — no stops on rev	£20	£75	£200
1697 — B	£12	£40	£150
1697 — C	£12	£40	£150

1697 Shilling of BRISTOL: B below bust

	F	VF	EF
1697 — E	£12	£60	£160
1697 — N	£15	£45	£160
1697 — y	£15	£45	£160
1697 — Y	£20	£50	£170
1697 3rd bust	£10	£20	£65
1697 — B	£15	£65	£225
1697 — C	£10	£45	£130
1697 — E	£15	£65	£200
1697 — N	£15	£50	£160
1697 — y	£15	£50	£160
1697 3rd bust var	£10	£25	£75
1697 — B	£15	£50	£150
1697 — C	£75	£125	£275
1698 —	£20	£65	£150
1698 — plumes	£75	£125	£400
1698 4th bust	£50	£140	£400
1699 —	£60	£150	£425
1699 5th bust	£30	£75	£200
1699 — plumes	£40	£180	£175
1699 — roses	£85	£175	£375
1700 — „	£10	£30	£90
1700 — no stops on rev	£20	£45	£150
1700 — plume	£650	*	*
1701 —	£35	£95	£200
1701 — plumes	£50	£120	£275

Anne 1702 shilling, VIGO below bust

ANNE

	F	VF	EF
1702 1ST BUST	£30	£75	£175

	F	VF	EF
1702 — plumes	£40	£95	£300
1702 — VIGO	£30	£65	£175
1703 2nd bust VIGO	£30	£70	£195
1704 —	£150	£450	*
1704 — plumes	£45	£125	£300
1705 —	£45	£125	£300
1705 — plumes	£30	£65	£200
1705 — r & p	£30	£65	£200
1707 — r & p	£30	£65	£200
1707 — E	£30	£60	£150
1707 — E★	£60	£100	£250
1707 3rd bust	£12	£25	£80
1707 — plumes	£30	£70	£175
1707 — E	£12	£50	£150
1707 Edin bust E★	*	*	*
1708 2nd bust E	£60	£165	*
1708 — E★	£35	£70	£225
1708/7 — E★	£40	£125	*
1708 — r & p	£40	£140	£350
1708 3rd bust	£10	£25	£90
1708 — plumes	£30	£65	£200
1708 — r & p	£30	£65	£200
1708 — E	£40	£90	*
1708 — E	£55	£120	*
1708 Edin bust E★	£25	£65	£225
1709 — — —	£30	£75	£225
1709 — E	£70	£140	£350
1709 3rd bust	£10	£25	£85
1710 — r & p	£20	£50	£165
1710 4th bust prf	*	*	*
1710 — r & p	£25	£65	£180
1711 3rd bust	£50	£90	£225
1711 4th bust	£10	£25	£85
1712 — r & p	£15	£30	£150
1713/2 — —	£20	£45	£150
1714 — —	£15	£45	£150

George I 1723 SS C shilling

GEORGE I

	F	VF	EF
1715 1st bust r & p	£15	£40	£140
1716 — —	£75	£200	£450
1717 — —	£15	£45	£160
1718 — —	£20	£50	£150
1719 — —	£60	£150	£250
1720 — —	£15	£35	£140
1720 — plain	£12	£30	£140
1720 — — large 0	£12	£30	£140
1721 — —	£150	£400	£700
1721 — r & p	£12	£35	£140
1721/0 — —	£12	£35	£140
1721/19	£15	£35	£140
1721/18	£15	£35	£140
1722 — —	£12	£35	£140
1723 — —	£10	£40	£150
1723 — SS C	£10	£25	£95
1723 — SS C French arms at date	£75	£140	£250
1723 2nd bust SS C	£10	£20	£100
1723 — r & p	£12	£65	£200
1723 — w.c.c.	£150	£300	£800
1724 — r & p	£12	£65	£200
1724 — w.c.c.	£150	£300	£800

	F	VF	EF	
1725 — r & p	£20	£70	£200	
1725 — no obv stops	£30	£90	£275	
1725 — w.c.c.	£250	£400	*	
1726 — r & p	*	*	*	
1726 — w.c.c.	£300	£500	*	
1727 — r & p	£400	*	*	
1727 — — no stops on obv ...	£250	*	*	

GEORGE II

	F	VF	EF	
1727 YH plumes	£45	£125	£240	
1727 — r & p	£35	£90	£200	
1728 —	£45	£100	£395	
1728 — r & p	£35	£80	£180	
1729 — —	£40	£90	£200	
1731 — —	£15	£70	£165	
1731 — plumes	£40	£125	£350	
1732 — r & p	£30	£80	£175	
1734 — —	£30	£70	£175	
1735 — —	£30	£70	£175	
1736 — —	£30	£70	£175	
1736/5 — —	£35	£80	£190	
1737 — —	£15	£65	£150	
1739 — roses	£10	£35	£120	
1741 — roses	£10	£40	£120	

1763 'Northumberland' Shilling

	F	VF	EF	
1743 OH roses	£10	£35	£125	
1745 —	£10	£35	£125	
1745 — LIMA	£12	£30	£125	
1746 — — LIMA	£35	£100	£300	
1746/5 — LIMA	£20	£120	£350	
1746 — proof	*	£250	£500	
1747 — roses	£10	£35	£100	
1750 —	£10	£35	£130	
1750/6 —	£12	£40	£130	
1750 — 5 over 4	£12	£35	£130	
1751 —	£15	£35	£145	
1758 —	£5	£15	£25	

1728 Young Head Shilling

GEORGE III

	F	VF	EF	Unc
1763 'Northumberland'	£125	£195	£300	£400
1786 proof or pattern	*	*	*	£2500
1787 no hearts	*	£4	£25	£35
1787 — no stop over head	£1.50	£12	£45	£65
1787 — no stops at date	£3	£20	£40	£70

	F	VF	EF	Unc
1787 — no stops on obv	£100	£300	£600	*
1787 hearts	*	£4	£25	£35
1798 'Dorrien and Magens'	*	*	£3250	£5000
1816	£1	£3	£35	£50
1817	£1	£3	£35	£50
1817 GEOE	£30	£70	£250	*
1818	£4	£20	£45	£90
1819	£1	£4	£40	£55
1819/8	*	*	£90	£90
1820	£1	£4	£40	£75

GEORGE IV

	F	VF	EF	Unc
1820 1st hd 1st rev pattern or prf	*	*	*	£1500
1821 1st hd 1st rev ...	£5	£10	£80	£130
1821 — proof	*	*	£175	£350
1823 — 2nd rev ...	£5	£30	£85	£185
1824 — —	£5	£12	£70	£130
1825 — —	£5	£12	£70	£130
1825 2nd hd	£5	£10	£70	£140
1826 —	£3	£10	£70	£110

George IV 1826 shilling

	F	VF	EF	Unc
1826 — proof	*	*	£75	£150
1827	£5	£20	£100	£160
1829	£4	£15	£85	£150

WILLIAM IV

	F	VF	EF	Unc
1831 proof	*	*	*	£275
1834	£3	£15	£70	£130
1835	£5	£20	£100	£180
1836	£3	£12	£70	£130
1837	£5	£15	£125	£275

William IV 1837 shilling

VICTORIA

	F	VF	EF	Unc
1838	£2	£11	£50	£90
1839	£2	£11	£65	£110
1839 2nd YH	£2	£7	£60	£80
1839 — proof	*	*	*	£225
1840	£7	£30	£90	£125
1841	£2	£11	£55	£140
1842	£2	£9	£55	£90
1843	£2	£11	£65	£100
1844	£1	£7	£55	£90
1845	£2	£10	£55	£90
1846	£1	£9	£55	£90
1848/6	£20	£70	£275	£425
1849	£2	£10	£65	£120

SHILLINGS

	F	VF	EF	Unc
1850	£125	£450	£900	*
1850/46	£125	£450	£900	*
1851	£14	£50	£200	*
1852	£1	£9	£55	£90
1853	£1	£9	£55	£90
1853 proof	*	*	*	£350
1854	£20	£90	£250	*
1855	£2	£9	£55	£90
1856	£2	£9	£55	£90
1857	£2	£9	£55	£90
1857 F:G:	*	*	*	*
1858	£2	£9	£50	£90
1859	£2	£9	£50	£90
1860	£4	£10	£75	£135
1861	£4	£10	£75	£135
1862	£6	£30	£90	£165

Victoria 1839 shilling

	F	VF	EF	Unc
1863	£8	£35	£150	£250
1864	£3	£7	£50	£90
1865	£3	£7	£50	£90
1866	£3	£7	£50	£90
1866 BBITANNIAR ...	*	*	£350	*
1867	£3	£7	£60	£110
1867 3rd YH, die no.	£150	£250	*	*
1868	£3	£7	£60	£110
1869	£3	£9	£70	£130
1870	£3	£9	£70	£125
1871	£3	£7	£37	£65
1872	£2	£6	£37	£65
1873	£2	£6	£37	£65
1874	£2	£6	£37	£65
1875	£2	£6	£37	£65
1876	£2	£8	£40	£80
1877 die no.	£1	£5	£35	£55
1877 no die no.	*	*	*	*
1878	£1	£5	£35	£60
1879 3rd YH	£10	£20	£85	*
1879 4th YH	£3	£9	£35	£70
1880	£1	£5	£25	£55
1880 longer line below SHILLING ...	*	*	*	*
1881	£1	£5	£25	£60
1881 longer line below SHILLING ...	£2	£8	£30	£60
1881 — large rev lettering	£2	£8	£25	£60
1882	£2	£9	£45	£110
1883	£1	£4	£30	£55
1884	£1	£4	£30	£55
1885	£1	£4	£30	£55
1886	£1	£4	£30	£55
1887	£1	£5	£40	£90
1887 JH	*	*	£5	£12
1887 proof	*	*	*	£80
1888	*	£3	£20	£45
1889	£12	£30	£150	£300
1889 large JH	*	£2	£15	£40
1890	*	£2	£20	£50
1891	*	£2	£20	£45
1892	*	£2	£20	£45

Victoria Jubilee Head and Old Head shillings

	F	VF	EF	Unc
1893 OH	*	£2	£12	£20
1893 — proof	*	*	*	£100
1893 small obv letters	*	£2	£15	£30
1894	*	£2	£15	£30
1895	*	£2	£15	£30
1896	*	£2	£15	£30
1897	*	£2	£15	£30
1898	*	£2	£15	£30
1899	*	£2	£15	£30
1900	*	£2	£15	£30
1901	*	£2	£15	£20

EDWARD VII

	F	VF	EF	Unc
1902	*	£2	£12	£18
1902 matt prf	*	*	£15	£20

Edward VII 1905 shilling

	F	VF	EF	Unc
1903	£3	£10	£75	£200
1904	£3	£10	£85	£225
1905	£25	£65	£375	*
1906	*	£2	£20	£45
1907	£1	£5	£25	£60
1908	£3	£10	£75	£200
1909	£1	£7	£90	£175
1910	*	£3	£15	£35

GEORGE V

	F	VF	EF	Unc
1911	*	*	£6	£18
1911 proof	*	*	*	£30
1912	*	*	£3	£45
1913	*	*	£20	£60
1914	*	*	£3	£12
1915	*	*	£2	£10
1916	*	*	£3	£12
1917	*	*	£3	£15
1918	*	*	£3	£15
1919	*	*	£6	£25
1920	*	*	£7	£20
1921	*	*	£7	£25

George V nickel trial shilling, 1924

		F	VF	EF	Unc
1922	... ...	*	*	£12	£35
1923	... ...	*	*	£7	£25
1923 nickel	... ...	*	*	£200	£350
1924	... ...	*	*	£7	£20
1924 nickel	... ...	*	*	£200	£350
1925	... ...	*	*	£12	£60
1926	... ...	*	*	£8	£35
1926 mod eff	... ...	*	*	£8	£25
1927 —	... ...	*	*	£8	£30
1927 new type	... ...	*	*	£4	£20
1927 — proof	... ...	*	*	*	£20
1928	... ...	*	*	£1	£10
1929	... ...	*	*	£2	£12
1930	... ...	*	*	£7	£20
1931	... ...	*	*	£3	£12
1932	... ...	*	*	£3	£12
1933	... ...	*	*	£3	£12
1934	... ...	*	*	£4	£25
1935	... ...	*	*	£1	£7
1936	... ...	*	*	£1	£5

GEORGE VI

		F	VF	EF	Unc
1937 Eng	... ...	*	*	£1	£5
1937 Eng prf	... ...	*	*	*	£7
1937 Scot	... ...	*	*	£1	£3
1937 Scot prf	... ...	*	*	*	£6
1938 Eng	... ...	*	*	£2	£15
1938 Scot	... ...	*	*	£2	£12
1939 Eng	... ...	*	*	£1	£5
1939 Scot	... ...	*	*	£1	£5
1940 Eng	... ...	*	*	£1	£5
1940 Scot	... ...	*	*	£1	£5
1941 Eng	... ...	*	*	£1	£4
1941 Scot	... ...	*	*	£2	£5
1942 Eng	... ...	*	*	£1	£3
1942 Scot	... ...	*	*	£1	£4
1943 Eng	... ...	*	*	£1	£3
1943 Scot	... ...	*	*	£1	£4
1944 Eng	... ...	*	*	*	£3
1944 Scot	... ...	*	*	*	£3
1945 Eng	... ...	*	*	*	£3
1945 Scot	... ...	*	*	*	£2
1946 Eng	... ...	*	*	*	£2
1946 Scot	... ...	*	*	*	£2
1947 Eng	... ...	*	*	*	£3
1947 Scot	... ...	*	*	*	£3

Reverses: English (left), Scottish (right)

		F	VF	EF	Unc
1948 Eng	... ...	*	*	*	£2
1948 Scot	... ...	*	*	*	£2
1949 Eng	... ...	*	*	*	£4
1949 Scot	... ...	*	*	*	£4
1950 Eng	... ...	*	*	*	£5
1950 Eng prf	... ...	*	*	*	£6
1950 Scot	... ...	*	*	*	£5
1950 Scot prf	... ...	*	*	*	£6
1951 Eng	... ...	*	*	*	£5
1951 Eng prf	... ...	*	*	*	£6
1951 Scot	... ...	*	*	*	£5
1951 Scot prf	... ...	*	*	*	£6

ELIZABETH II

		F	VF	EF	Unc
1953 Eng	... ...	*	*	*	£1
1953 Eng prf	... ...	*	*	*	£5
1953 Scot	... ...	*	*	*	£1

SHILLINGS

		F	VF	EF	Unc
1953 Scot prf	... ...	*	*	*	£5
1954 Eng	... ...	*	*	*	£1
1954 Scot	... ...	*	*	*	£1
1955 Eng	... ...	*	*	*	£1
1955 Scot	... ...	*	*	*	£1
1956 Eng	... ...	*	*	*	£2
1956 Scot	... ...	*	*	*	£6
1957 Eng	... ...	*	*	*	£2
1957 Scot	,... ...	*	*	*	£5
1958 Eng	... ...	*	*	*	£6
1958 Scot	... ...	*	*	*	£1

Reverses: English (left), Scottish (right)

		F	VF	EF	Unc
1959 Eng	... ...	*	*	*	£1
1959 Scot	... ...	*	*	*	£20
1960 Eng	... ...	*	*	*	£1
1960 Scot	... ...	*	*	*	£2
1961 Eng	... ...	*	*	*	£0.80
1961 Scot	... ...	*	*	*	£5
1962 Eng	... ...	*	*	*	*
1962 Scot	... ...	*	*	*	*
1963 Eng	... ...	*	*	*	*
1963 Scot	... ...	*	*	*	*
1964 Eng	... ...	*	*	*	*
1964 Scot	... ...	*	*	*	*
1965 Eng	... ...	*	*	*	*
1965 Scot	... ...	*	*	*	*
1966 Eng	... ...	*	*	*	*
1966 Scot	... ...	*	*	*	*

Sixpences

CROMWELL				F	VF	EF
1658	... ...			*	*	of the
						highest rarity
1658 Dutch copy	... ...			£500	£900	*

CHARLES II

1674	... ...	£15	£60	£160
1675	... ...	£10	£50	£160
1675/4	... ...	£20	£75	£185
1676	... ...	£20	£75	£185
1676/5	... ...	£20	£75	£185
1677	... ...	£10	£50	£160
1678/7	... ...	£20	£75	£180

Charles II 1678 sixpence

1679	... ...	£20	£75	£185
1680	... ...	£30	£95	£250

SIXPENCES

	F	VF	EF
1681	£10	£45	£150
1682	£30	£85	£195
1682/1	£14	£55	£150
1683	£10	£55	£135
1684	£18	£65	£180

James II 1688 sixpence

JAMES II

	F	VF	EF
1686 early shields	£40	£95	£300
1687 —	£35	£100	£350
1687/6	£35	£100	£350
1687 later shield	£35	£95	£300
1687/6	£40	£110	£375
1688 —	£45	£125	£400

WILLIAM AND MARY

	F	VF	EF
1693	£35	£125	£325
1693 3 upside down... ...	£45	£150	£350
1694	£60	£175	£375

William and Mary 1694 sixpence

WILLIAM III

	F	VF	EF
1695 1st bust early harp ...	£5	£25	£95
1696 — —	£3	£10	£40
1696 — — no obv stops ...	£5	£25	£95
1696/5	£10	£40	£125
1696 — — B	£4	£25	£100
1696 — — C	£4	£25	£100
1696 — — E	£8	£40	£110
1696 — — N	£4	£35	£100
1696 — — y	£5	£25	£90
1696 — — Y	£10	£40	£110
1696 — later harp	£10	£60	£165
1696 — — B	£22	£80	£200
1696 — — C	£25	£95	£225
1696 — — N	£22	£85	£200
1696 2nd bust	£100	£225	£475
1697 1st bust early harp ...	£2	£10	£45
1697 — — B	£7	£30	£100
1697 — — C	£7	£30	£100
1697 — — E	£8	£40	£100
1697 — — N	£5	£30	£100
1697 — — y	£10	£40	£100
1697 2nd bust	£30	£110	£250
1697 3rd bust later harp ...	£3	£12	£45
1697 — — B	£10	£35	£120
1697 — — C	£30	£60	£125
1697 — — E	£15	£40	£125
1697 — — Y	£15	£45	£110
1698 — —	£10	£35	£90
1698 — — plumes	£28	£80	£175
1699 — —	£45	£125	£275
1699 — plumes	£35	£75	£175

William III 1699 sixpence, plumes

	F	VF	EF
1699 — — roses	£40	£100	£225
1700	£8	£15	£55
1701	£12	£25	£110

ANNE

	F	VF	EF
1703 VIGO	£15	£30	£90
1705	£20	£75	£165
1705 plumes	£15	£60	£160
1705 roses & plumes	£15	£50	£130
1707 —	£15	£45	£80
1707 plain	£10	£15	£50
1707 E	£10	£30	£120

Anne 1707 sixpence, E below bust

	F	VF	EF
1707 plumes	£15	£35	£110
1708 plain	£5	£15	£55
1708 E	£15	£50	£150
1708/7 E	£45	£100	£225
1708 E★	£15	£60	£200
1708/7 E★	£45	£95	£195
1708 Edin bust E ★	£18	£65	£170
1708 plumes	£15	£45	£150
1710 roses & plumes	£15	£50	£160
1711 plain	£5	£15	£50

George I 1717 sixpence

GEORGE I

	F	VF	EF
1717	£15	£70	£200
1720/17	£15	£70	£200
1723 SS C, small letters on obv	£6	£18	£75
1723 SS C, large letters both sides	£8	£20	£70
1726 roses & plumes ...	£25	£90	£250

GEORGE II

	F	VF	EF
1728 YH	£15	£60	£160
1728 — plumes	£10	£50	£140
1728 — r & p	£10	£45	£125
1731 — —	£10	£45	£125
1732 — —	£10	£45	£125
1734 — —	£15	£60	£140
1735 — —	£15	£50	£125
1736 — —	£10	£40	£125
1739 — roses	£5	£30	£90

	F	VF	EF
1741 — —	£5	£25	£90
1743 OH	£5	£25	£90
1745 — —	£5	£25	£90
1745/3 — —	£15	£35	£125
1745 — LIMA	£6	£18	£65
1746 — LIMA	£6	£18	£65
1746 — plain proof	*	*	£300

George II 1746 sixpence

	F	VF	EF
1750	£5	£15	£65
1751	£10	£25	£80
1757	£2	£5	£15
1757	£2	£5	£15
1758/7	£5	£12	£20

GEORGE III

	F	VF	EF	Unc
1787 hearts	£1	£3	£12	£30
1787 no hearts ...	£1	£3	£12	£30
1816	£1	£3	£20	£45
1817	£1	£3	£20	£45
1818	£3	£9	£35	£75
1819	£1	£3	£20	£50
1819 small 8 ...	£3	£8	£30	£85
1820	£1	£3	£20	£60
1820 1 inverted ...	£20	£95	£225	£450

GEORGE IV

	F	VF	EF	Unc
1820 1st hd 1st rev ...	*	*	*	£850
(pattern or proof)				
1821 1st hd 1st rev ...	£2	£5	£60	£100
1821 — — BBITANNIAR	£50	£100	£250	£400
1824 1st hd 2nd rev	£2	£6	£55	£100
1825 — —	£2	£5	£65	£100
1826 — —	£10	£35	£150	£225
1826 2nd hd 3rd rev	£2	£5	£60	£95

George IV 1825 sixpence

	F	VF	EF	Unc
1826 — — proof ...	*	*	*	£125
1827	£10	£35	£100	£225
1828	£3	£12	£90	£135
1829	£2	£10	£65	£125

WILLIAM IV

	F	VF	EF	Unc
1831	£2	£9	£45	£95
1831 proof	*	*	*	£150
1834	£2	£9	£45	£95
1835	£2	£15	£70	£120
1836	£5	£35	£90	£135
1837	£2	£20	£90	£150

VICTORIA

	F	VF	EF	Unc
1838	£1	£5	£50	£75
1839	£1	£5	£50	£75
1839 proof	*	*	*	£150

	F	VF	EF	Unc
1840	£1	£7	£45	£80
1841	£1	£7	£45	£80
1842	£2	£9	£60	£110
1843	£1	£5	£50	£85
1844	£1	£5	£40	£70
1845	£1	£5	£40	£70
1846	£1	£5	£40	£70
1848	£5	£20	£175	£325
1848/6	£6	£25	£175	£325
1848/7	£6	£25	£175	£325
1850	£2	£10	£55	£110
1850 5 over 3 ...	£10	£25	£150	£275
1851	£2	£8	£40	£85
1852	£2	£6	£40	£80
1853	£1	£4	£40	£75
1853 proof	*	*	*	£250
1854	£15	£50	£275	£400
1855	£1	£5	£40	£65
1856	£1	£5	£40	£65
1857	£1	£7	£45	£70
1858	£1	£7	£45	£70
1859	£1	£7	£40	£65
1859/8	£1	£7	£45	£75
1860	£1	£7	£45	£75
1862	£10	£35	£200	£350
1863	£5	£17	£90	£150
1864	£1	£6	£40	£70
1865	£1	£6	£40	£70
1866	£1	£6	£40	£70
1866 no die no. ...	*	*	*	*
1867	£4	£14	£50	£85
1868	£4	£14	£50	£85
1869	£4	£15	£60	£95
1870	£4	£14	£60	£100
1871	£2	£5	£40	£55
1871 no die no. ...	£3	£10	£40	£65
1872	£2	£6	£35	£65
1873	£1	£5	£30	£50
1874	£1	£5	£30	£50
1875	£1	£5	£30	£60
1876	£4	£14	£40	£75
1877	£2	£5	£30	£50
1877 no die no. ...	£2	£5	£30	£50
1878	£2	£5	£30	£50
1878 DRITANNIAR ...	£30	£90	£250	£375
1879 die no.	£4	£8	£40	£70
1879 no die no. ...	£2	£4	£30	£45
1880 2nd YH ...	£1	£4	£18	£35
1880 3rd YH ...	£1	£3	£15	£30
1881	£1	£3	£15	£30
1882	£1	£8	£30	£60
1883	£1	£3	£15	£30
1884	£1	£3	£15	£30
1885	£1	£3	£15	£30
1886	£1	£3	£15	£30
1887 YH	£1	£3	£15	£30
1887 JH shield rev ...	£1	£2	£4	£12

1887 Jubilee Head sixpence, withdrawn type

	F	VF	EF	Unc
1887 — proof	*	*	*	£75
1887 new rev	£1	£2	£3	£10
1888	£1	£3	£12	£35
1889	£1	£3	£12	£35

SIXPENCES

	F	VF	EF	Unc
1890	£1	£3	£12	£35
1891	£1	£3	£12	£35
1892	£1	£3	£12	£35
1893	£100	£300	£750	*
1893 OH	£1	£3	£15	£35
1893 proof	*	*	*	£85
1894	£1	£3	£20	£35
1895	£1	£3	£20	£35
1896	£1	£3	£20	£35
1897	£1	£3	£18	£30
1898	£1	£3	£18	£30
1899	£1	£3	£20	£35
1900	£1	£3	£18	£30
1901	£1	£3	£18	£30

EDWARD VII

	F	VF	EF	Unc
1902	*	£2	£8	£15
1902 matt proof	*	*	*	£20
1903	£1	£5	£20	£40
1904	£2	£6	£22	£55
1905	£2	£6	£22	£45
1906	£1	£3	£12	£35
1907	£1	£5	£12	£35
1908	£2	£7	£22	£50
1909	£1	£4	£18	£40
1910	£1	£4	£9	£25

GEORGE V

	F	VF	EF	Unc
1911	*	*	£5	£20
1911 proof	*	*	*	£30
1912	*	*	£12	£35
1913	*	*	£15	£35
1914	*	*	£4	£14
1915	*	*	£4	£14
1916	*	*	£4	£14
1917	*	*	£12	£30
1918	*	*	£5	£12
1919	*	*	£6	£15
1920	*	*	£8	£25
1920 debased	*	*	£8	£25
1921	*	*	£6	£20
1922	*	*	£5	£20
1923	*	*	£7	£30
1924	*	*	£6	£20
1925	*	*	£6	£20
1925 new rim	*	*	£5	£18
1926 new rim	*	*	£8	£25
1926 mod effigy	*	*	£5	£18
1927	*	*	£3	£15
1927 new rev prf	*	*	*	£18
1928	*	*	£1	£7
1929	*	*	£1	£7
1930	*	*	£1	£8
1931	*	*	£1	£7
1932	*	*	£5	£15
1933	*	*	£1	£6
1934	*	*	£3	£10

George V 1935 sixpence

	F	VF	EF	Unc
1935	*	*	£1	£5
1936	*	*	£1	£4

GEORGE VI

	F	VF	EF	Unc
1937	*	*	*	£2
1937 proof	*	*	*	£4
1938	*	*	£2	£6
1939	*	*	£1	£3
1940	*	*	£1	£3
1941	*	*	£1	£3
1942	*	*	£1	£2
1943	*	*	*	£2
1944	*	*	*	£1
1945	*	*	*	£1
1946	*	*	*	£1
1947	*	*	*	£1
1948	*	*	*	£1
1949	*	*	*	£2
1950	*	*	*	£2
1950 proof	*	*	*	£3.50
1951	*	*	*	£2
1951 proof	*	*	*	£3.50
1952	*	£2	£8	£20

ELIZABETH II

	F	VF	EF	Unc
1953	*	*	*	£0.50
1953 proof	*	*	*	£2
1954	*	*	*	£2
1955	*	*	*	£0.60
1956	*	*	*	£0.60
1957	*	*	*	£0.30
1958	*	*	*	£2
1959	*	*	*	£0.20
1960	*	*	*	£1.50
1961	*	*	*	£1.50
1962	*	*	*	£0.25
1963	*	*	*	*
1964	*	*	*	*
1965	*	*	*	*
1966	*	*	*	*
1967	*	*	*	*

Groats (fourpences)

William IV 1836 groat
Earlier dates are included in Maundy sets

WILLIAM IV

	F	VF	EF	Unc
1836	*	£2	£12	£35
1836 proof	*	*	*	£350
1837	*	£3	£15	£50

Victoria 1842 groat

VICTORIA

	F	VF	EF	Unc
1838	*	£2	£10	£35
1838 8 over 8 on side	£1	£3	£20	£60
1839	*	£3	£15	£55
1839 proof	*	*	*	£125
1840	*	£2	£15	£55
1840 narrow 0	£2	£6	£30	*
1841	£1.25	£7	£20	£60
1841 I for last 1	*	*	*	*
1842	*	£3	£15	£50

	F	VF	EF	Unc
1842/1	£3	*	*	*
1843	*	£3	£15	£45
1844	*	£4	£25	£60
1845	*	£3	£15	£50
1846	*	£3	£15	£50
1847/6	£20	£35	£90	£135
1848 small date	*	£2	£15	£50
1848 large date	*	£2	£15	£50
1848/6	£1.50	£6	£18	£60
1848/7	£1.50	£6	£18	£60
1849	*	£4	£18	£60
1849/8	£1.75	£8	£40	£80
1851	£1.75	£15	£120	£200
1852	£40	*	*	*
1853	£20	£50	£200	*
1853 proof	*	*	*	£250
1854	*	£2	£15	£55
1854 5 over 3	*	£2	£18	£70
1855	*	£2	£15	£55
1857 proof	*	*	*	£700
1862 proof	*	*	*	£450
1888 JH	£1	£2	£12	£35

Silver threepences

Earlier dates are included in Maundy sets

WILLIAM IV

	F	VF	EF	Unc
1834	*	£3	£15	£60
1835	*	£3	£15	£60
1836	*	£3	£15	£50
1837	*	£6	£20	£65

Victoria threepence of 1848

VICTORIA

	F	VF	EF	Unc
1838	*	£4	£20	£45
1839	*	£7	£25	£55
1840	*	£5	£20	£55
1841	*	£5	£20	£55
1842	*	£5	£20	£60
1843	*	£5	£15	£40
1844	*	£6	£25	£60
1845	*	£3	£15	£35
1846	*	£6	£28	£70
1847	*	*	*	£350
1848	*	*	£275	*
1849	*	£6	£30	£70
1850	*	£3	£20	£45
1851	*	£3	£20	£45
1852	*	*	£275	*
1853	*	£6	£32	£90
1854	*	£3	£20	£45
1855	*	£5	£20	£50
1856	*	£2.50	£15	£40
1857	*	£5	£18	£42
1858	*	£3	£18	£42
1858/6	*	*	*	*
1859	*	£3	£18	£32
1860	*	£3	£18	£32
1861	*	£3	£18	£32
1862	*	£3	£15	£40
1863	*	£6	£25	£55
1864	*	£3	£20	£45
1865	*	£6	£25	£55
1866	*	£3	£20	£50
1867	*	£3	£25	£55

	F	VF	EF	Unc
1868	*	£3	£20	£50
1868 RRITANNIAR ...	£15	£35	£150	*
1869[1]	*	*	£25	*
1870	*	£2	£15	£35
1871	*	£2	£15	£35
1872	*	£1.50	£12	£35
1873	*	£1.25	£12	£30
1874	*	£1.25	£12	£30
1875	*	£1.25	£10	£27
1876	*	£1.25	£10	£27
1877	*	£1.25	£10	£27
1878	*	£1.25	£10	£27
1879	*	£1.25	£10	£27
1880	*	£1.25	£10	£27
1881	*	£1	£10	£22
1882	*	£1.50	£12	£40
1883	*	£1	£8	£20
1884	*	£1	£8	£20
1885	*	£1	£8	£20
1886	*	£1	£8	£20
1887 YH	*	£3	£15	£35
1887 JH	*	£1.50	£3	£7
1887 proof	*	*	*	£40
1888	*	£1.50	£7	£20
1889	*	£1	£6	£17
1890	*	£1	£6	£17
1891	*	£1	£6	£17
1892	*	£1	£7	£17
1893	£10	£20	£60	£125
1893 OH	*	*	£3	£12
1893 OH proof ...	*	*	*	£50
1894	*	*	£4	£18
1895	*	*	£4	£18
1896	*	*	£4	£18
1897	*	*	£3	£15
1898	*	*	£3	£15
1899	*	*	£3	£15
1900	*	*	£3	£15
1901	*	*	£2	£12

EDWARD VII

	F	VF	EF	Unc
1902	*	*	£4	£10
1902 matt proof ...	*	*	*	£12
1903	*	£1.50	£6	£20
1904	*	£6	£14	£35
1905	*	£6	£14	£35
1906	*	£3	£10	£30
1907	*	£1.50	£5	£20
1908	*	£1.50	£6	£22
1909	*	£2	£6	£22
1910	*	£1.25	£4	£18

George V 1927 threepence, acorns on reverse

GEORGE V

	F	VF	EF	Unc
1911	*	*	£3	£12
1911 proof	*	*	*	£25
1912	*	*	£3	£12
1913	*	*	£3	£12
1914	*	*	£2	£10
1915	*	*	£2	£10
1916	*	*	£1.50	£8
1917	*	*	£1.50	£8
1918	*	*	£2	£8
1919	*	*	£2	£8

SILVER THREEPENCES

	F	VF	EF	Unc
1920	*	*	£2	£10
1920 debased	*	*	£2	£10
1921	*	*	£2	£12
1922	*	*	£2	£12
1925	*	£1	£6	£18
1926	*	£3	£10	£25
1926 mod effigy ...	*	£1	£6	£20
1927 new rev prf	*	*	*	£30
1928	*	£2	£6	£20
1930	*	£1.50	£5	£12
1931	*	*	£1	£6
1932	*	*	£1	£6
1933	*	*	£1	£6
1934	*	*	£1	£6
1935	*	*	£1	£6
1936	*	*	£1	£6

GEORGE VI

	F	VF	EF	Unc
1937	*	*	£0.75	£1.50
1937 proof... ...	*	*	*	£5
1938	*	*	£0.50	£1
1939	*	£1	£3	£5
1940	*	*	£1	£2
1941	*	*	£1	£2
1942	£1	£2	£6	£8
1943	£1	£3	£7	£9
1944[2]	£1.50	£5	£12	£20
1945[2]	*	*	*	*

[1]Threepences issued for use in the Colonies.
[2]All specimens of 1945 were thought to have been melted down but it appears that one or two still exist.

Small silver for Colonies

These tiny coins were struck for use in some of the Colonies — they were never issued for circulation in Britain. However, they are often included in collections of British coins and it is for this reason that prices for them are given here.

TWOPENCES

Other dates are included in Maundy sets.

VICTORIA

	F	VF	EF	Unc
1838	*	£2	£8	£15
1838 2nd 8 like S ...	*	£6	£17	£30
1848	*	£2	£8	£15

THREEHALFPENCES

WILLIAM IV

	F	VF	EF	Unc
1834	*	£2	£18	£30
1835	*	£2	£18	£30
1935/4...	*	£8	£25	£60
1836	*	£2	£18	£30
1837	£6	£15	£70	£125

VICTORIA

	F	VF	EF	Unc
1838	*	£2	£8	£20
1839	*	£1.25	£8	£15
1840	*	£5	£15	£35
1841	*	£2	£9	£25
1842	*	£2	£9	£20
1843	*	£1	£6	£18

1843 threehalfpence

	F	VF	EF	Unc
1843/34	£2	£8	£20	£50
1860	£1	£3	£15	£30
1862	£1	£3	£15	£30
1870 proof...	*	*	*	£350

Maundy sets

EF prices are for evenly matched sets

Charles II 1670 Maundy set. The denomination is shown by one one, two, three or four Cs on the reverses

CHARLES II

	F	VF	EF
1670	£45	£75	£200
1671	£45	£60	£150
1672	£45	£70	£200
1673	£45	£60	£150
1674	£45	£60	£150
1675	£45	£60	£150
1676	£45	£60	£150
1677	£45	£60	£150
1678	£45	£70	£250
1679	£45	£65	£150
1680	£45	£60	£150
1681	£45	£75	£225
1682	£45	£70	£175
1683	£45	£60	£150
1684	£45	£70	£175

JAMES II

	F	VF	EF
1686	£45	£75	£150
1687	£45	£75	£175
1688	£45	£75	£175

WILLIAM AND MARY

	F	VF	EF
1689	£250	£375	£600
1691	£75	£110	£225
1692	£90	£125	£275
1693	£80	£120	£300
1694	£75	£110	£200

WILLIAM III

	F	VF	EF
1698	£60	£90	£200
1699	£60	£100	£250
1700	£60	£100	£225
1701	£60	£100	£200

COINS MARKET VALUES

ANNE	F	VF	EF
1703	£50	£80	£200
1705	£50	£80	£175
1706	£50	£75	£140
1708	£55	£85	£200
1709	£50	£75	£150
1710	£55	£85	£200
1713	£50	£75	£150

GEORGE I	F	VF	EF
1723	£50	£80	£150
1727	£50	£80	£150

GEORGE II	F	VF	EF
1729	£40	£65	£150
1731	£40	£65	£150
1732	£35	£60	£130
1735	£35	£60	£130
1737	£35	£60	£130
1739	£35	£60	£130
1740	£35	£60	£130
1743	£40	£70	£150
1746	£35	£60	£120
1760	£45	£70	£150

GEORGE III	F	VF	EF	Unc
1763	£20	£35	£85	*
1766	£25	£45	£85	*
1772	£25	£45	£85	*
1780	£25	£45	£85	*
1784	£25	£45	£85	£125
1786	£25	£45	£85	£125
1792 wire type	*	£60	£150	£200

1792 wire type Maundy set, so called because of the wire-like style of the figures of value

			F	VF	EF	Unc
1795	... ...		*	£45	£75	£130
1800	... ...		£30	*	*	£110
1817 ...	... ...		*	£40	£75	£125
1818 ...	... ...		*	£40	£75	£125
1820 ...	... ...		*	£40	£75	£125

GEORGE IV			F	VF	EF	Unc
1822	... ...		*	£40	£80	£130
1823	... ...		*	£35	£70	£120
1824	... ...		*	£35	£75	£125
1825 ...	... ...		*	£35	£70	£120
1826 ...	... ...		*	£35	£70	£120
1827 ...	... ...		*	£35	£70	£120
1828 ...	... ...		*	£35	£70	£120
1829 ...	... ...		*	£35	£70	£120
1830 ...	... ...		*	£35	£70	£120

WILLIAM IV			F	VF	EF	Unc
1831	... ...		*	£45	£80	£135
1831 proof	... ...		*	*	*	£400
1832	... ...		*	£45	£75	£150
1833	... ...		*	£45	£75	£135
1834	... ...		*	£45	£75	£135
1835	... ...		*	£45	£75	£135

	F	VF	EF	Unc
1836	*	£45	£85	£175
1837	*	£45	£85	£175

VICTORIA	F	VF	EF	Unc
1838			£45	£75
1839			£45	£65
1839 proof			*	£300
1840			£45	£75
1841			£45	£80
1842			£45	£90
1843			£45	£75
1844			£45	£75
1845			£45	£65
1846			£45	£90
1847			£45	£75

Victoria 1847 Young Head Maundy set

		EF	Unc
1848		£45	£85
1849		£45	£90
1850		£45	£70
1851		£45	£70
1852		£45	£70
1853		£60	£110
1853 proof		*	£500
1854		£45	£65
1855		£45	£60
1856		£45	£65
1857		£45	£70
1858		£45	£70
1859		£45	£65
1860		£45	£70
1861		£45	£70
1862		£45	£70
1863		£45	£70
1864		£45	£70
1865		£45	£70
1866		£45	£70
1867		£45	£70
1868		£45	£70
1869		£45	£70
1870		£40	£65
1871		£40	£65
1872		£40	£65
1873		£40	£65
1874		£40	£65
1875		£40	£65
1876		£40	£65
1877		£40	£65
1878		£40	£65
1879		£40	£65
1880		£40	£65
1881		£40	£65
1882		£40	£65
1883		£40	£65
1884		£40	£65
1885		£40	£65
1886		£40	£65
1887		£40	£65
1888 JH		£45	£60

MAUNDY SETS

	EF	Unc
1889	£45	£60
1890	£45	£60
1891	£45	£60
1892	£45	£60
1893 OH	£30	£40
1894	£30	£40
1895	£30	£40
1896	£30	£40
1897	£30	£40
1898	£30	£40
1899	£30	£40
1900	£30	£40
1901	£30	£40

EDWARD VII

	EF	Unc
1902	£25	£35
1902 matt proof	*	£45
1903	£28	£40
1904	£28	£40
1905	£28	£40
1906	£28	£40
1907	£28	£40
1908	£28	£40
1909	£40	£55
1910	£45	£60

GEORGE V

	EF	Unc
1911	£30	£50
1911 proof	£*	£55
1912	£30	£50
1913	£30	£50
1914	£35	£60
1915	£30	£50
1916	£30	£50
1917	£30	£50
1918	£30	£50
1919	£30	£50
1920	£30	£50
1921	£30	£50
1922	£30	£50
1923	£30	£50
1924	£30	£50
1925	£30	£50
1926	£30	£50
1927	£30	£50
1928	£30	£50
1929	£35	£55
1930	£30	£50
1931	£30	£50
1932	£30	£50
1933	£30	£50
1934	£30	£50
1935	£35	£50
1936	£40	£60

GEORGE VI

	EF	Unc
1937	*	£45
1938	*	£45
1939	*	£45
1940	*	£45
1941	*	£45
1942	*	£45
1943	*	£45
1944	*	£45
1945	*	£45
1946	*	£45
1947	*	£50
1948	*	£50
1949	*	£50
1950	*	£50
1951	*	£50
1952	*	£50

ELIZABETH II

	EF	Unc
1953	£125	£200
1954	*	£45
1955	*	£45
1956	*	£45
1957	*	£45
1958	*	£45
1959	*	£45
1960	*	£45

1960 Maundy set of Elizabeth II

	EF	Unc
1961	*	£50
1962	*	£50
1963	*	£50
1964	*	£50
1965	*	£50
1966	*	£50
1967	*	£50
1968	*	£50
1969	*	£50
1970	*	£50
1971	*	£50
1972	*	£50
1973	*	£50
1974	*	£50
1975	*	£50
1976	*	£50
1977	*	£50
1978	*	£50
1979	*	£50
1980	*	£50
1981	*	£50
1982	*	£50
1983	*	£50
1984	*	£50
1985	*	£50
1986	*	£50
1987	*	£50
1988	*	£50
1989	*	£50
1990	*	£50
1991	*	£50
1992	*	£50
1993	*	£50
1994	*	£50
1995	*	£50
1996	*	£75

Nickel-brass threepences

1937 threepence of Edward VIII, extremely rare

1937-dated Edward VIII threepences, struck in 1936 ready for issue, were melted after Edward's abidcation. A few, however, escaped into circulation to become highly prized collectors' pieces. George VI 1937 threepences were struck in large numbers.

EDWARD VIII	F	VF	EF	BU
1937	*	* Highest rarity *		

1937 threepence of George VI

GEORGE VI				
1937	*	*	£1	£2
1938	*	*	£3	£10
1939	*	*	£4	£20
1940	*	*	£2	£4
1941	*	*	£1	£3
1942	*	*	£1	£2
1943	*	*	£1	£2
1944	*	*	£1	£3
1945	*	*	*	£3
1946	£1	£5	£30	£150
1948	*	*	£4	£6
1949	£1	£4	£30	£125
1950	*	*	£8	£25
1951	*	*	£8	£25
1952	*	*	*	£1.50

ELIZABETH II				
1953	*	*	*	£1
1954	*	*	*	£2
1955	*	*	*	£2
1956	*	*	£1	£2
1957	*	*	*	£2
1958	*	*	£2	£4
1959	*	*	*	£2
1960	*	*	*	£1.25
1961	*	*	*	*
1962	*	*	*	*
1963	*	*	*	*
1964	*	*	*	*
1965	*	*	*	*
1966	*	*	*	*
1967	*	*	*	*

Copper twopence

George III 1797 'cartwheel' twopence

GEORGE III	F	VF	EF	BU
1797	£6	£25	£135	£350

Copper pennies

GEORGE III	F	VE	EF	BU
1797 10 leaves	£1	£5	£65	£225
1797 11 leaves	£1	£6	£65	£225

1797 'cartwheel' penny

1806	£1	£4	£45	£120
1806 no incuse curl	£1	£4	£45	£125
1807	£1	£4	£45	£125

1806 penny of George III

GEORGE IV				
1825	£3	£8	£60	£175
1826	£1	£5	£50	£150
1826 thin line down				
St Andrew's cross	£2	£7	£55	£165
1826 thick line	£3	£8	£55	£175
1827	£80	£200	£950	*

COPPER PENNIES

William IV 1831 penny

WILLIAM IV		F	VF	EF	BU
1831	... ...	£3	£15	£125	*
1831 .w.w incuse	...	£4	£20	£145	*
1831 w.w incuse		£5	£25	£150	*
1834	... ...	£5	£25	£150	*
1837	... ...	£7	£30	£175	*

Victoria 1841 copper penny

VICTORIA		F	VF	EF	Unc
1839 proof	... ...	*	*	£125	£225
1841	... ...	£8	£22	£75	*
1841 no colon after REG	... ...	£1	£3	£30	£100
1843	... ...	£8	£30	*	*
1843 no colon after REG	... ...	£12	*	*	*
1844	... ...	£3	£7	£30	£100
1845	... ...	£4	£9	£50	£135
1846 DEF far colon	... ...	£2	£8	£30	£100
1846 DEF close colon	... ...	£3	£9	£40	£110
1847 DEF close colon	... ...	£3	£7	£30	£100
1847 DEF far colon	... ...	£3	£7	£35	£100

		F	VF	EF	BU
1848	... ...	£2	£4	£25	£90
1848/6	... ...	£7	£18	£75	£150
1848/7	... ...	£2	£8	£35	£100
1849	... ...	£30	£75	£225	£475
1851 DEF far colon	... ...	£3	£7	£40	£100
1851 DEF close colon	... ...	£4	£8	£40	£110
1853 OT	... ...	£1	£4	£22	£85
1853 colon nearer F		£2	£5	£28	£100
1853 PT	... ...	£2	£5	£20	£75
1854 PT	... ...	£2	£5	£20	£75
1854/3	... ...	£12	£40	*	*
1854 OT	... ...	£2	£4	£20	£75
1855 OT	... ...	£2	£4	£20	£75
1855 PT	... ...	£2	£4	£20	£75
1856 PT	... ...	£12	£40	£100	£250
1856 OT	... ...	£8	£30	£85	£225
1857 OT	... ...	£1	£2	£18	£70
1857 PT	... ...	£1	£2	£18	£70
1857 small date	...	£1	£3	£18	£70
1858	... ...	£1	£2	£15	£70
1858 small date	...	£1	£2	£18	£80
1858/3 now thought to be 1858 9/8 (see below)					
1858/7	... ...	£1	£2.50	£17	£70
1858/6	... ...	£7	£20	£70	*
1858 no ww	... ...	£0.75	£2	£17	£70
1858 no ww (large 1 and 5, small 8s)		£2	£4	£18	£80
1858 9/8?	... ...	£4	£15	£35	£95
1858 9/8? large rose		£5	£18	£40	£110
1859	... ...	£1	£4	£30	£80
1859 small date	...	£2	£5	£35	£90
1860/59	... ...	*	£250	£600	*

Bronze pennies

For fuller details of varieties in bronze pennies see English Copper, Tin and Bronze Coins in the British Museum 1558-1958 *by C. W. Peck;* The Bronze Coinage of Great Britain *by M. J. Freeman and* The British Bronze Penny 1860-1970 *by Michael Gouby.*

VICTORIA	F	VF	EF	BU
1860 RB, sheild crossed with incuse treble lines	*	£5	£25	£75
1860 RB, shield crossed with close double raised lines	£4	£8	£30	£85
1860 RB, double lines, but farther apart, rock to left of lighthouse	£10	£40	£100	£250
1860 RB obv/TB rev ...	£30	£80	£500	*
1860 TB obv/RB rev ...	£30	£70	£450	*

1860 penny, toothed border on obverse

| 1860 TB, L.C. WYON on truncation, L.C.W. incuse below shield ... ... | * | £4 | £25 | £75 |

	F	VF	EF	BU
1860 TB, same obv but L.C.W. incuse below foot	£15	£30	£175	£350
1860 TB, as previous but heavy flan of 170 grains	*	£175	*	*
1860 TB, LC, WYON below truncation, L.C.W. incuse below shield ...	*	£3	£25	£70
1860 TB, no signature on obv. L.C.W. incuse below shield	*	£5	£40	£85
1861 L.C. WYON on truncation, L.C.W. incuse below shield	£7	£20	£70	£150
1861 same obv. no signature on rev	*	£6	£25	£70
1861 L.C. WYON below truncation, L.C.W. incuse below shield	*	£5	£25	£70
1861 similar, but heavy flan (170 grains)	*	*	*	*
1861 same obv but no signature on rev	*	£4	£25	£80
1861 no signature on obv, L.C.W. incuse below shield	*	£4	£25	£75
1861 — 6/8	£15	£45	£250	£400
1861 no signature either side	£1	£4	£25	£70
1862	£1	£3	£25	£70
1862 sm date figs ...	£12	£36	*	*
1863	£1	£3	£25	£75
1863 slender 3 ...	*	*	*	*
1863 die no. (2,3 or 4) below date	£100	£175	*	*
1864 plain 4	£6	£20	£150	£650
1864 crossiet 4	£8	£25	£180	£750
1865	*	£7	£30	£80
1865/3	£10	£45	£225	£500
1866	*	£4	£25	£85
1867	*	£5	£30	£90
1868	£3	£15	£85	£250
1869	£10	£75	£450	£800
1870	£2	£15	£100	£225
1871	£6	£30	£150	£350
1872	*	£4	£25	£75
1873	*	£4	£25	£75
1874 (1873 type) ...	*	£4	£25	£75
1874 H (1873 type) ...	*	£3	£25	£80
1874 new rev, lighthouse tall and thin	£5	£12	£25	£80
1874 H as previous ...	£2	£5	£25	£70
1874 new obv/1873 rev	*	£3	£25	£70
1874 H as previous ...	*	£3	£20	£70
1874 new obv/new rev	*	£3	£25	£70
1874 H as previous ...	*	£3	£25	£60
1875	*	£4	£25	£65
1875 H	£10	£45	£200	£500
1876 H	*	£3	£12	£50
1877	*	£4	£12	£60
1878	*	£6	£20	£70
1879	*	*	£12	£60
1880	*	*	£20	£80
1881 (1880 obv) ...	*	*	£20	£60
1881 new obv	*	£12	£35	£100
1881 H	*	*	£12	£60
1882 H	*	*	£14	£60
1882 no H	£50	£175	£500	£1100
1883	*	*	£10	£60
1884	*	*	£10	£55
1885	*	*	£10	£55
1886	*	*	£8	£50
1887	*	*	£9	£50

BRONZE PENNIES

	F	VF	EF	BU
1888	*	*	£80	£50
1889 14 leaves	*	*	£10	£55
1889 15 leaves	*	*	£10	£55
1890	*	*	£10	£45
1891	*	*	£10	£45
1892	*	*	£10	£50
1893	*	*	£10	£50
1894	*	*	£18	£70
1895 2mm	*	£25	£150	£250

Victoria old head penny of 1895

	F	VF	EF	BU
1895	*	*	£5	£35
1896	*	*	£3	£30
1897	*	*	£2.50	£25
1897 higher horizon	£2	£10	£125	£300
1898	*	£1.25	£6.50	£35
1899	*	£1	£3.50	£30
1900	*	*	£2.50	£12
1901	*	*	£1	£8

Edward VII 1902 penny, low horizon

EDWARD VII

	F	VF	EF	BU
1902 low horizon ...	*	£5	£25	£45
1902	*	*	£2	£8
1903	*	*	£2	£15
1904	*	*	£5	£20
1905	*	*	£3	£18
1906	*	*	£3	£15
1907	*	*	£2	£15

BRONZE PENNIES

	F	VF	EF	BU
1908	*	*	£5	£20
1909	*	*	£4	£20
1910	*	*	£3	£15

GEORGE V

	F	VF	EF	BU
1911	*	*	£3	£15
1912	*	*	£3	£15
1912 H	*	*	£12	£40
1913	*	*	£6	£30
1914	*	*	£3	£20
1915	*	*	£3.50	£20
1916	*	*	£3	£20
1917	*	*	£3	£20
1918	*	*	£3.50	£20
1918 H	*	£8	£75	£150
1918 KN	*	£10	£95	£200
1919	*	*	£3	£22
1919 H	*	£2	£60	£165
1919 KN	*	£6.50	£100	£275
1920	*	*	£3.50	£15
1921	*	*	£2	£15
1922	*	*	£7	£20
1922 rev as 1927 . . . ext rare			*	*
1926	*	*	£10	£35
1926 mod effigy ...	£2	£25	£250	£600
1927	*	*	£3	£12
1928	*	*	£1	£10
1929	*	*	£1	£10
1930	*	*	£3.50	£15
1931	*	*	£4	£15
1932	*	*	£6	£30
1933			highest rarity	
1934	*	*	£6	£20
1935	*	*	£1	£5
1936	*	*	*	£4

GEORGE VI

	F	VF	EF	BU
1937	*	*	*	£1
1938	*	*	*	£1
1939	*	*	*	£2
1940	*	*	*	£5
1944	*	*	*	£4
1945	*	*	*	£3
1945 9 double (2 dies)	£2	£5	£20	*
1946	*	*	*	£2
1947	*	*	*	£1
1948	*	*	*	£2
1949	*	*	*	£2

Obverse used for George VI pennies from 1949 to 1951. IND: IMP: is omitted from the legend

	F	VF	EF	BU
1950	£1.50	£5	£9	£18
1951	£1.75	£5	£8	£15

ELIZABETH II

	F	VF	EF	BU
1953	*	£1	£1.80	£3
1953 proof	*	*	*	£5

	Fair	F	VF	EF
1961	*	*	*	£0.50
1962	*	*	*	*
1963	*	*	*	*
1964	*	*	*	*
1965	*	*	*	*
1966	*	*	*	*
1967	*	*	*	*

Copper halfpennies

All copper unless otherwise stated

Charles II 1675 halfpenny

CHARLES II

	Fair	F	VF	EF
1672	£4	£12	£50	£350
1672 CRAOLVS ...	£15	£40	£90	£400
1673	£4	£12	£50	£325
1673 CRAOLVS ...	£15	£30	£75	£350
1673 no stops on reverse	£5	£15	£60	£325
1673 no stops on obverse	£5	£15	£65	£325
1675	£5	£15	£65	£325
1675 no stops on obverse	£6	£18	£65	£325

James II 1685 tin halfpenny

JAMES II

	Fair	F	VF	EF
1685 (tin)	£25	£50	£200	£800
1686 (tin)	£30	£60	£250	£800
1687 (tin)	£25	£50	£200	£800
1687 D over D	*	*	*	*

WILLIAM AND MARY

	Fair	F	VF	EF
1689 (tin) ET on right	£60	£150	£400	*
1689 (tin) ET on left ...	*	*	*	*
1690 (tin) dated on edge	£20	£45	£250	£900
1691 (tin) date in exergue and on edge	£25	£40	£250	£900

	Fair	F	VF	EF
1691/2 (tin) 1691 in exergue 1692 on edge	£28	£45	£250	£900
1692 (tin) date in exergue and on edge	£15	£35	£250	*
1694	£5	£10	£50	£375

William and Mary 1694 halfpenny

	Fair	F	VF	EF
1694 GVLIEMVS ...	*	*	*	*
1694 no stop after MARIA	£12	£25	£75	£400
1694 BRITANNIA with last I over A	£10	£40	*	*
1694 no stop on reverse	£5	£12	£50	£350

WILLIAM III
Type 1 (date in exergue)

	Fair	F	VF	EF
1695	£3	£10	£40	£400
1695 thick flan	£25	£50	£120	*
1695 BRITANNIA ...	£3	£15	*	*
1695 no stop on reverse	£2	£14	£60	*
1696	£2	£14	£65	*
1696 GVLIEMVS, no stop on reverse ...	£15	*	*	*
1696 TERTVS	£5	£30	£120	*
1696 obv struck from doubled die	£10	£30	*	*
1697	£2	£10	£60	*
1697 no stops either side	£3	£16	£65	*
1697 I of TERTIVS over E	£5	£40	*	*
1697 GVLILMVS no stop on reverse ...	£6	£30	*	*
1697 no stop after TERTIVS	£2	£20	*	*
1698	£4	£16	*	*

Type 2 (date in legend)

	Fair	F	VF	EF
1698	£5	£20	£90	*
1699	£1	£25	£50	*
1699 BRITANNIA ...	£1.75	£10	£50	*
1699 GVLIEMVS ...	£3	£15	£60	*

Type 3 (Britannia's hand on knee, date in exergue)

	Fair	F	VF	EF
1699	£5	£12	£60	*
1699 stop after date...	£7	£20	*	*
1699 BRITANNIA ...	£5	£12	£60	*
1699 GVILELMVS ...	£10	*	*	*
1699 TERTVS	£15	*	*	*
1699 no stop on reverse	£15	*	*	*
1699 no stops on obverse	£2	£8	£50	*

COPPER HALFPENNIES

	Fair	F	VF	EF
1699 no stops after GVLIELMVS.	£2	£8	£50	*
1700	£2	£8	£50	£500
1700 no stops on obverse	£2	£8	£50	*
1700 no stop after GVLIELMVS	£2	£9	£60	*
1700 BRITANNIA ...	£1	£7	£50	*
1700 no stop on reverse	£1	£8	£60	*
1700 GVLIELMS ...	£3	£16	£65	*
1700 GVLIEEMVS ...	£1.75	£12	£60	*
1700 TER TIVS ...	£1	£10	£60	*
1700 1 of TERTIVS over V	£10	£25	*	*
1701 BRITANNIA ...	£1	£7	£50	*
1701 no stops on obverse	£2	£10	£50	*
1701 GVLIELMVS TERTIVS	£5	£18	£70	*

GEORGE I
Type 1

	Fair	F	VF	EF
1717	*	£4	£60	£200
1717 no stops on obverse	£1	£10	£75	*
1718	*	£4	£60	£250
1718 no stops on obverse	*	*	*	*
1719 on larger flan of type 2	*	*	*	*
1719 — edge grained	*	*	*	*

Type 2

	Fair	F	VF	EF
1719 both shoulder straps ornate	£1	£4	£35	£225
1719 — edge grained	*	*	*	*
1719 bust with left strap plain	£1	£6	£50	*
1719 — edge grained	*	*	*	*
1720	*	£4	£35	£225
1721	*	£4	£35	£225
1721/0	£1	£6	£35	*
1721 stop after date...	*	£6	£35	£225
1722	*	£6	£35	£225
1722 GEORGIVS ...	£1.50	£8	£35	*
1723	*	£6	£35	£225
1723 no stop on reverse	*	£8	£35	£250
1724	*	£6	£35	£225

George II 1729 halfpenny

GEORGE II
Young Head

	Fair	F	VF	EF
1729	*	£4	£17	£120
1729 no stop on reverse	£1	£5	£20	£110

COPPER HALFPENNIES

	Fair	F	VF	EF
1730	*	£4	£10	£100
1730 GEOGIVS, no stop on reverse ...	£1.25	£6	£14	£110
1730 stop after date...	*	£7	£13	£110
1730 no stop afer REX or on reverse ...	£1.25	£8	£14	£110
1731	*	£4	£10	£110
1731 no stop on reverse	*	£6	£14	£90
1732	*	£3	£12	£90
1732 no stop on reverse	*	£6	£15	£90
1733	*	£2	£12	£90
1733 only obverse stop before REX ...	*	£4	£15	£90
1734	*	£2	£12	£90
1734/3...	*	£4	£18	£90
1734 no stops on obverse	*	£2	£15	£85
1735	*	£2	£12	£85
1736	*	£2	£12	£85
1737	*	£2	£12	£85
1738	*	£2	£12	£85
1739	*	£2	£12	£85

Old Head

		F	VF	EF
1740		*	£2	£12	£80
1742		*	£4	£13	£80
1742/0...		*	£8	£20	£80
1743		*	£2	£10	£80
1744		*	£2	£10	£80
1745		*	£2	£10	£80
1746		*	£3	£10	£80
1747		*	£3	£10	£80
1748		*	£2	£7	£80
1749		*	£2	£7	£80
1750		*	£3	£10	£80
1751		*	£3	£10	£80
1752		*	£3	£10	£80
1753		*	£3	£10	£80
1754		*	£3	£10	£80

GEORGE III

	F	VF	EF	BU
1770	£1	£6	£60	£200
1771	£1	£4	£50	£175
1771 no stop on reverse	£1.75	£6	£50	£175
1771 ball below spear head	£1.50	£6	£50	£175
1772	£1.50	£6	£50	£175
1772 GEORIVS ...	£7	£20	£85	£225
1772 ball below spear head	£1.50	£6	£50	£175
1772 no stop on reverse	£2	£10	£55	£175
1773	£1.50	£6	£50	£175
1773 no stop after REX	£2	£10	£50	£175
1773 no stop on reverse	£2	£11	£55	£200
1774	£2	£10	£50	£175
1775	£2.50	£10	£50	£175
1799 5 incuse gunports	*	*	£12	£50
1799 6 relief gunports	*	*	£12	£50
1799 9 relief gunports	*	*	£15	£50
1799 no gunports ...	*	*	£12	£50
1799 no gunports and raised line along hull	*	*	£12	£50
1806 no berries on olive branch	*	*	£12	£65

	F	VF	EF	BU
1806 line under SOHO 3 berries	*	*	£12	£65
1807 similar but double-cut border bead between B and R	*	*	£12	£65

GEORGE IV

		F	VF	EF	BU
1825		*	£2	£35	£95

George IV 1826 halfpenny

		F	VF	EF	BU
1826 two incuse lines down cross		*	£2	£35	£110
1826 raised line down centre of cross ...		*	£4	£37	£100
1827		*	£2	£35	£100

WILLIAM IV

		F	VF	EF	BU
1831		*	£5	£45	£125
1834		*	£5	£45	£125
1837		*	£4	£40	£125

VICTORIA

	F	VF	EF	BU
1838	*	£1	£12	£50
1839 proof	*	*	*	£125
1839 proof, rev inv ...	*	*	*	£150
1841	*	£1	£10	£50
1843	£3	£8	£40	£100
1844	£1	£3	£30	£80
1845	£18	£40	£250	£650
1846	£2	£4	£30	£65
1847	£1	£6	£30	£65
1848	£1	£3	£30	£65
1848/3	£15	£25	*	*
1848/7	£1	£2	£12	£60
1851	£1	£2	£12	£65
1851 7 incuse dots on and above shield ...	*	£2	£12	£65
1852	*	£2	£12	£70
1852 7 incus dots on and above shield ...	*	£2	£12	£60
1853	*	£1	£10	£50
1853/2	£3	£8	£45	*
1854	*	£1	£8	£50

Victoria 1854 copper halfpenny

		F	VF	EF	BU
1855		*	£1	£8	£50
1856		*	£2	£15	£65
1857		*	£2	£15	£50

	F	VF	EF	BU
1857 7 incuse dots on and above shield ...	*	£2	£12	£60
1858	*	£2	£12	£60
1858/6...	£2	£8	£30	£85
1858/7...	£1	£3	£15	£60
1858 small date... ...	£1	£3	£15	£60
1859	£1	£2	£15	£60
1859/8...	£3	£8	£40	*
1860	*	*	*	£2000

Bronze halfpennies

VICTORIA

	F	VF	EF	BU
1860	*	£3	£15	£45
1860 TB 7 berries in wreath	*	£3	£15	£45
1860 TB 4 berries in wreath	*	£3	£15	£45
1860 TB similar but centres of four of leaves are double incuse lines ...	£5	£8	£25	£80
1861 obv 4 berries, 15 leaves, raised leaf centres, rev L.C.W. on rock ...	*	£2	£15	£60
1861 same obv, rev no signature ...			ext. rare	
1861 same but lighthouse has no vertical lines	£6	£10	£25	£85
1861 obv 4 berries, 4 double incuse leaf centres, rev L.C.W. on rock ...	*	£1.50	£12	£40
1861 same obv, rev no signature ...	£5	£8	£25	£85
1861 obv 7 double incuse leaf centres, rev L.C.W. on rock ...	*	£2	£12	£50
1861 same obv, rev no signature ...	*	£1.50	£12	£35
1861 obv 16 leaves, rev lighthouse has rounded top	*	£1.50	£12	£35
1861 same obv, rev lighthouse has pointed top	*	£1.50	£12	£35
1862 L.C.W. on rock ...	*	£4	£10	£60
£861 no signature ...	*	£2	£10	£35
1862 letter (A, B or C) left of lighthouse base ...	£35	£85	£350	*
1863 ...	*	£2	£12	£35
1864	*	£4	£15	£60
1865	*	£2	£15	£60
1865/3	£10	£40	£150	*
1866	*	£1.50	£12	£45
1867	*	£2	£12	£50
1868	*	£2	£12	£50

BRONZE HALFPENNIES

	F	VF	EF	BU
1869	*	£5	£18	£70
1870	*	£4	£15	£50
1871	£10	£25	£100	£295
1872	*	£2	£12	£35
1873	*	£5	£18	£60
1874	*	£8	£25	£75
1874H	*	£2	£12	£35
1875	*	£2	£12	£35
1875H	*	£6	£16	£50
1876H	*	£2	£10	£40
1877	*	£2	£10	£40
1878	*	£15	£35	£150
1879	*	£2	£10	£35
1880	*	£2	£10	£35
1881	*	£2	£10	£35
1881H	*	£2	£10	£35
1882H	*	£2	£10	£35
1883	*	£2	£10	£35
1984	*	£2	£10	£35
1885	*	£2	£10	£35
1886	*	£1.50	£10	£35
1887	*	£1	£10	£30
1888	*	£1	£10	£30
1889	*	£1	£10	£30
1889/8	*	£8	£20	£60
1890	*	£1	£6	£35
1891	*	£1	£8	£30
1892	*	£1	£7	£30
1893	*	*	£7	£30
1894	*	£2	£10	£35
1895 OH	*	*	£2	£30
1896	*	*	£2	£30
1897 normal horizon ...	*	*	£2	£28
1897 higher horizon...	*	*	£2	£28
1898	*	*	£5	£30
1899	*	*	£3	£30
1900	*	*	£1	£10
1901	*	*	£1	£10

EDWARD VII

	F	VF	EF	BU
1902 low horizon ...	*	£5	£28	£65
1902	*	*	£2	£10
1903	*	*	£3	£25
1904	*	*	£5	£30
1905	*	*	£3	£20
1906	*	*	£3	£20
1907	*	*	£3	£20
1908	*	*	£3	£20
1909	*	*	£4	£25
1910	*	*	£4.25	£25

GEORGE V

	F	VF	EF	BU
1911	*	*	£2.75	£12
1912	*	*	£2	£12

Victoria 1871 bronze halfpenny

George V 1912 halfpenny

	F	VF	EF	BU
1913	*	*	£5	£20
1914	*	*	£3	£15
1915	*	*	£3	£15

BRONZE HALFPENNIES

	Fair	F	VF	EF
1916	*	*	£2	£15
1917	*	*	£2	£15
1918	*	*	£2	£15
1919	*	*	£2	£15
1920	*	*	£2	£15
1921	*	*	£2	£15
1922	*	*	£3	£15
1923	*	*	£2	£15
1924	*	*	£3	£15
1925	*	*	£4	£15
1925 mod effigy ...	*	*	£4	£20
1926	*	*	£4	£15
1927	*	*	£2.50	£12
1928	*	*	£2	£12
1929	*	*	£2	£12
1930	*	*	£2	£12
1931	*	*	£2	£12
1932	*	*	£2	£12
1933	*	*	£2	£15
1934	*	*	£2	£15
1935	*	*	£1.75	£7
1936	*	*	£1.50	£5

GEORGE VI

	Fair	F	VF	EF
1937	*	*	*	£1
1938	*	*	*	£2
1939	*	*	*	£2
1940	*	*	*	£2.75
1941	*	*	*	£3
1942	*	*	*	£1
1943	*	*	*	£1
1944	*	*	*	£2
1945	*	*	*	£1
1946	*	*	£2	£4
1947	*	*	*	£3
1948	*	*	*	£1
1949	*	*	*	£1
1950	*	*	*	£4
1951	*	*	*	£4.50
1952	*	*	*	£1.50

ELIZABETH II

	Fair	F	VF	EF
1953	*	*	*	£1.75
1954	*	*	*	£2.50
1955	*	*	*	£3
1956	*	*	*	£3
1957	*	*	*	£1
1958	*	*	*	£0.50
1959	*	*	*	£0.25
1960	*	*	*	£0.20
1962	*	*	*	*
1963	*	*	*	*
1964	*	*	*	*
1965	*	*	*	*
1966	*	*	*	*
1967	*	*	*	*

Copper farthings

Copper unless otherwise stated

CHARLES II

	Fair	F	VF	EF
1671 patterns only ...	*	*	£100	£350
1672	£1	£4	£25	£200
1672 no stops on obverse	£2.75	£6	£35	£225
1672 loose drapery at Britannia's elbow	£2	£6	£35	£225
1673	£1	£5	£20	£200

Charles II 1673 farthing

	Fair	F	VF	EF
1673 CAROLA ...	*	*	*	*
1673 BRITINNIA ...	*	*	*	*
1673 no stops on obverse	£2	£5	£45	£225
1673 no stop on reverse	£2	£5	£45	£225
1674	£1	£4	£35	£200
1675	£1	£2.75	£25	£200
1675 no stop after CAROLVS	*	*	*	*
1676	*	*	*	*
1679	£1.50	£4	£45	£225
1679 no stop on reverse	*	*	*	*
1684 (tin) various edge readings	£12	£25	£150	£800
1685 (tin)	£15	£70	£175	£825

JAMES II

	Fair	F	VF	EF
1684 (tin)	£30	£80	£175	£800
1685 (tin) various edge readings	£20	£35	£120	*
1686 (tin) various edge readings	£20	£50	£125	*
1687 (tin)	*	*	*	*
1687 (tin) draped bust, various readings	*	*	*	*

WILLIAM AND MARY

	Fair	F	VF	EF
1689 (tin) date in exergue and on edge, many varieties ...	£15	£45	£135	*
1689/90 (tin) 1689 in exergue, 1690 on edge	*	*	*	*
1689/90 (tin) 1690 in exergue, 1689 on edge	*	*	*	*
1690 (tin) various types	£12	£30	£125	£800
1691 (tin) small and large figures	£12	£30	£125	£800
1692 (tin)	£15	£35	£125	£800
1694 many varieties...	£2	£15	£45	£250

WILLIAM III
Type 1, date in exergue

	Fair	F	VF	EF
1695	£3	£7	£50	£350
1695 M over V ...	*	*	*	*
1696	£2	£5	£45	£350
1697	£2	£5	£40	£350

William III 1697 farthing

	Fair	F	VF	EF
1698	£5	£12	£50	*
1699	£2	£5	£45	£400
1700	£2	£5	£35	£375

Type 2, date in legend	Fair	F	VF	EF
1698	£3.50	£10	£40	£400
1699	£1.50	£10	£35	£400

Anne 1714 pattern farthing

ANNE

	Fair	F	VF	EF
1714 patterns (F)	£40	£150	£225	£350

George I 'dump' farthing of 1717

GEORGE I
'Dump Type'

	Fair	F	VF	EF
1717	£12	£20	£70	£250
1718 silver proof ...	*	*	*	£650

Larger flan

	Fair	F	VF	EF
1719 large lettering on obverse	£3	£10	£30	£200
1719 small lettering on obverse	£3	£10	£45	£225
1719 — last A of BRITANNIA over I ...	*	*	*	*

George I 1719 farthing

	Fair	F	VF	EF
1719 legend continuous over bust	£7	£25	*	*
1720 large lettering on obverse	£3	£10	£30	£200
1720 small lettering on obverse	£2	£5	£28	£200
1721	£2	£4	£25	£200
1721/0	£10	£30	*	*
1722 large lettering on obverse	£4	£10	£30	£200
1722 small lettering on obverse	£3	£8	£28	£200
1723	£2	£5	£25	£195
1723 R of REX over R	£8	*	*	*
1724	£5	£10	£30	£225

George II 1730 farthing

GEORGE II	Fair	F	VF	EF
1730	*	£2.50	£10	£110
1731	*	£2.75	£12	£110
1732	*	£5	£12	£110
1733	*	£2.25	£9	£110
1734	*	£2	£10	£110
1734 no stops on obverse	*	£3	£14	£120
1735	*	£2	£10	£110
1735 3 over 3	*	£8	£25	£120
1736	*	£2.25	£10	£110
1736 triple tie-riband	*	*	*	*
1737 sm date	*	£2	£10	£110
1737 lge date	*	£2.25	£12	£110
1739	*	£2	£10	£80
1739/5...	*	*	*	*
1741 Old Head	*	£3	£10	£50
1744	*	£2	£10	£45
1746	*	£1.50	£9	£45
1746 V over U	*	*	*	*
1749	*	£1.25	£8	£45
1750	*	£2	£8	£45
1754/0...	*	£12	£35	*
1754	*	£1.25	£8	£40

GEORGE III	F	VF	EF	BU
1771	*	£15	£65	£165
1773	*	£2.25	£35	£135
1774	*	£2.25	£35	£135
1775	*	£2.50	£40	£135
1799	*	*	£5	£50
1806	*	£1	£8	£50
1807	*	£2	£10	£45

GEORGE IV	F	VF	EF	BU
1821	*	£1	£20	£50
1822	*	£1	£20	£50
1823	*	£2	£20	£50
1825	*	£2	£20	£50
1825 D of DEI over U	£2	£5	£50	*
1826 date on rev	*	£1	£20	£50
1826 date on obv ...	*	£2	£25	£65
1826 I for 1 in date ...	*	*	*	*
1827	*	£2	£25	£65
1828	*	£2	£30	£90
1829	*	£3	£30	£90
1830	*	£2	£25	£75

WILLIAM IV	F	VF	EF	BU
1831	*	£2	£30	£90
1834	*	£2	£30	£90
1835	*	£2	£35	£110
1836	*	£2	£35	£110
1837	*	£2	£30	£90

VICTORIA	F	VF	EF	BU
1838	*	£2	£8	£40
1839	*	£2	£6	£35

COPPER FARTHINGS

	F	VF	EF	BU
1840	*	£2	£8	£40
1841	*	£2	£5	£30
1842	*	£4	£12	£45
1843	*	£1.75	£5	£35
1843 I for 1...	*	£5	£22	£100
1844	£10	£30	£150	*
1845	*	£3	£10	£50
1846	*	£5	£15	£60
1847	*	£2	£8	£50
1848	*	£3	£10	£55
1849	*	£7	£36	£175
1850	*	£2	£8	£50
1851	*	£6	£20	£90
1851 D over D	£5	*	*	*
1852	*	£7	£20	£100
1853 w.w. raised ...	*	£1	£6	£35
1853 ww inc	*	£2	£8	£40
1854 ww inc	*	£2	£8	£40
1855 ww inc	*	£2	£8	£45
1855 w.w. raised ...	*	£4	£12	£50
1856	*	£3	£20	£60
1856 R over E	£5	*	*	*
1857	*	£1.25	£5	£30
1858	*	£1	£5	£30
1859	*	£7	£20	£70
1860 proof...	*	*	*	£3500

Bronze farthings

VICTORIA	F	VF	EF	BU
1860 RB	*	£2.25	£10	£30
1860 TB/RB (mule)	£25	£60	£100	*
1860 TB	*	£1	£8	£30
1861	*	£1	£7	£30
1862 small 8	*	£1.25	£7	£25
1862 large 8	*	£2.50	£9	£28
1863	£8.50	£20	£50	*
1864	*	£1.25	£7	£28
1865 large 8	*	£1	£7	£28
1865—5/2	*	£2.75	£8	£30
1865—5/3	*	£2	£10	£35
1865 small 8	*	£1	£6	£30
1865—5/3	*	£2	£12	£35
1866	*	*	£6	£25
1867	*	£1	£6	£25
1868	*	£1.25	£8	£28
1869	*	£1.60	£9	£35
1872	*	£2.25	£9	£28
1873	*	£1.75	£5	£28
1874 H...	*	£1.60	£5	£25
1874 H both Gs over	£30	*	*	*
1875 5 berries/large date	£5	£10	£20	*
1875 5 berries/small date	*	*	*	*
1875 4 berries/small date	£6	£12	£25	*
1875 H 4 berries/ small date	*	*	£4	£25
1876 H...	*	£5.25	£14	£40
1877 proof...	*	*	*	£1450
1878	*	*	£5	£25
1879	*	£1	£6	£25
1879 large 9	*	£1.50	£7	£25
1880 4 berries	*	£1.60	£7	£25
1880 3 berries	*	£5	£12	£40
1881 4 berries	*	£5	£15	£40
1881 3 berries	*	£2	£6	£18

	F	VF	EF	BU
1881 H 3 berries ...	*	£2.25	£6	£20
1882 H...	*	£1.50	£5	£20
1883	*	£2.50	£8	£30
1884	*	*	£3	£20
1885	*	*	£3	£20
1886	*	*	£3	£20
1887	*	*	£7	£22
1888	*	*	£5	£22
1890	*	*	£5	£22
1891	*	*	£5	£22
1892	*	£3	£9	£30
1893	*	*	£2	£18
1894	*	*	£2	£22
1895	*	£7	£25	£80
1895 OH	*	*	£1	£15
1896	*	*	£0.75	£12

Victoria 1896 Old Head farthing

	F	VF	EF	BU
1897 bright finish ...	*	*	£2	£15
1897 black finish higher horizon ...	*	*	£1	£12
1898	*	*	£1.25	£15
1899	*	*	£1	£10
1900	*	*	£1	£10
1901	*	*	£1	£8

Edward VII 1907 farthing

EDWARD VII				
1902	*	*	£1.25	£6
1903 low horizon ...	*	*	£1.75	£10
1904	*	*	£2	£10
1905	*	*	£2	£10
1906	*	*	£1.75	£10
1907	*	*	£1.75	£10
1908	*	*	£1.50	£10
1909	*	*	£1.50	£10
1910	*	*	£3	£12

GEORGE V				
1911	*	*	*	£4
1912	*	*	*	£4
1913	*	*	*	£4
1914	*	*	*	£4
1915	*	*	*	£4
1916	*	*	*	£4
1917	*	*	*	£4
1918 black finish	*	*	*	£6
1918 bright finish	*	*	*	£2
1919	*	*	*	£2
1920	*	*	*	£4
1921	*	*	*	£3
1922	*	*	*	£4
1923	*	*	*	£4
1924	*	*	*	£4
1925	*	*	*	£4

COINS MARKET VALUES

	F	VF	EF	BU
1926 modified effigy	*	*	*	£4
1927	*	*	*	£4
1928	*	*	*	£2
1929	*	*	*	£2
1930	*	*	*	£2
1931	*	*	*	£2
1932	*	*	*	£2
1933	*	*	*	£2
1934	*	*	*	£3
1935	*	*	£1.50	£5
1936	*	*	*	£1

George VI 1937 farthing, wren on reverse

GEORGE VI
	F	VF	EF	BU
1937	*	*	*	£1
1938	*	*	*	£2
1939	*	*	*	£1
1940	*	*	*	£2
1941	*	*	*	£1
1942	*	*	*	£1
1943	*	*	*	£1
1944	*	*	*	£1
1945	*	*	*	£1
1946	*	*	*	£1
1947	*	*	*	£1
1948	*	*	*	£1
1949	*	*	*	£1
1950	*	*	*	£1
1951	*	*	*	£1
1952	*	*	*	£1

ELIZABETH II
	F	VF	EF	BU
1953	*	*	*	£0.50
1954	*	*	*	£0.35
1955	*	*	*	£0.35
1956	*	*	*	£1

Fractions of farthings

COPPER HALF FARTHINGS

GEORGE IV
	F	VF	EF	BU
1828 Britannia breaks legend	£3	£6	£30	£95
1828 Britannia below legend	£5	£8	*	*
1830 lge date	£3	£7	£35	£100
1830 sm date	£4	£10	*	*

WILLIAM IV
	F	VF	EF	BU
1837	£12	£40	£225	*

Victoria 1839 half farthing

BRONZE FARTHINGS

VICTORIA
	F	VF	EF	BU
1839	*	£2	£15	£50
1842	*	£2	£10	£40
1843	*	*	£1	£10
1844	*	*	£1	£8
1844 E over N ...	£3	£12	£50	*
1847	*	£3	£10	£40
1851	*	£3	£12	£45
1852	*	£3	£20	£50
1853	*	£4	£35	£75
1854	*	£4	£40	£95
1856	*	£5	£50	£110
1856 large date ...	£6	£25	*	*
1868 bronze proof ...	*	*	*	£150
1868 copper-nickel proof	*	*	*	£300

COPPER THIRD FARTHINGS

GEORGE IV
	F	VF	EF	BU
1827	*	£3	£12	£45

WILLIAM IV
	F	VF	EF	BU
1835	*	£3	£15	£50

VICTORIA
	F	VF	EF	BU
1844	*	£8	£25	£50
1844 RE for REG ...	£15	£30	£75	*
1844 large G in REG...	*	£8	£25	£50

BRONZE THIRD FARTHINGS

VICTORIA
	F	VF	EF	BU
1866	*	*	£4	£20
1868	*	*	£3	£20
1876	*	*	£4	£25
1878	*	*	£3	£20
1881	*	*	£4	£17
1884	*	*	£2	£10
1885	*	*	£2	£10

Edward VII 1902 third farthing

EDWARD VII
	F	VF	EF	BU
1902	*	*	£1	£5

GEORGE V
	F	VF	EF	BU
1913	*	*	£2	£7

COPPER QUARTER FARTHINGS

VICTORIA
	F	VF	EF	BU
1839	£3	£10	£20	£50

Victoria 1839 quarter farthing

	F	VF	EF	BU
1851	£4	£12	£28	£60
1852	£3	£10	£20	£50
1853	£5	£12	£25	£60
1868 bronze-proof ...	*	*	*	£200
1868 copper-nickel proof	*	*	*	£350

Decimal coinage

f denotes face value

ELIZABETH II

BRITANNIAS

A new United Kingdom gold bullion coin introduced in the autumn of 1987 contains one ounce of 22ct gold and has a face value of £100. There are also half ounce, quarter ounce and one-tenth ounce versions, with face values of £50, £25 and £10 respectively. All are legal tender.

The Britannia coins bear a portrait of The Queen on the obverse and the figure of Britannia on the reverse.

	BU
1987, 1988, 1989, 1991, 1992, 1993, 1994, 1995 1oz, proof	£450
1987, 1988, 1989, 1991, 1992 ½oz, proof ...	*
1987, 1988, 1989, 1991, 1992 ¼oz, proof ...	*
1987, 1988, 1989, 1991, 1992 ¹⁄₁₀oz, proof	£65

(½ and ¼oz issued only in sets)

FIVE POUNDS

1984 gold, BU	£400
1985 — —	£425
1986 — —	£425
1987 — new uncoupled effigy	£425
1988 — —	£425
1989 — BU, 500th anniversary of the sovereign	£450
1990 gold, BU	£435
1990 Queen Mother's 90th birthday, gold, proof	£575
1990 — silver, proof	£28.75
1990 — cu-ni, BU	£8.95
1991 gold, BU	£450
1992 gold, BU	£450
1993 40th Anniversary of The Coronation gold, proof	£700
1993 silver, proof, cu-ni	£10
1993 gold, BU	£550
1994 gold, BU	£500
1995 gold, BU	£535
1996 Queen's 70th birthday, gold, proof ...	£645
1996 Queen's 70th birthday, gold, BU ...	£575
1996 Queen's 70th birthday, silver, proof	£33
1996 Queen's 70th birthday, cu-ni, BU ...	£10

(Gold versions also listed in FIVE POUNDS section of milled gold.) In 1984 the Royal Mint issued the first of an annual issue of Brilliant Uncirculated £5 coins. These bear the letter 'U' in a circle.

TWO POUNDS

	BU
1983 gold, proof	£225
1986 Commonwealth Games (Nickel brass), unc in folder	£6
1986 — silver unc	£15
1986 — — proof	£25
1986 gold, proof	£250
1987 gold, proof	£250
1988 gold, proof	£250
1989 Bill of Rights, in folder, BU	£6
1989 — silver, proof	£22.50
1989 Claim of Right, in folder, BU	£6
1989 – silver, proof	£22.50
(For 1989 £2 piedforts see sets)	
1989 500th anniversary of the sovereigh, gold, proof	£300
1990 gold, proof	£275
1991 proof	£275
1993 gold, proof	£305
1994 Bank of England, gold, proof ...	£425
1994 —, gold 'mule', proof	£600
1994 – silver, proof	£27
1994 silver piedfort, proof	£50
1994, in folder, BU	£8
1995 50th Anniversary of end of Second World War, silver, proof	£27
1995, ditto, in folder, BU	£8
1995 —, silver, piedfort, proof ...	£50
1995 —, gold, proof	£325
1995 50th Anniversary of United Nations, gold, proof	£300
silver, proof, ditto in folder ...	£6
1995 —, silver, piedfort, proof	£50
1995 50th Anniversary of UN, proof ...	£300
1996 European Football Championship ...	£350
1996 European Football, gold, proof ...	£350
1996 European Football, silver, proof ...	£27
1996 European Football, silver, piedfort	£50
1996 European Football, in folder, BU ...	£6

(Gold versions are also listed in TWO POUNDS section of milled gold.)

ONE POUND

1983	£2
1983 Unc, in folder	£5
1983ssilver, proof	£30
1983 — — piedfort	£120
1984 Scottish reverse	£2
1984 — Unc, in album	£5
1984 — silver, proof	£20
1984 — — piedfort	£50
1985 New portrait, Welsh reverse ...	£2
1985 — — Unc, in wallet	£5
1985 — — silver, proof	£22
1985 — — piedfort	£50
1986 — Northern Ireland reverse	£2
1986 — Unc, in folder	£5
1986 — silver, proof	£25
1986 — — — piedfort	£50
1987 English reverse	£2
1987 — Unc, in folder	£3
1987 — silver proof	£20
1987 — — piedfort	£50
1988 Royal Arms reverse	£2
1988 — Unc, in folder	£5
1988 — silver, proof	£30
1988 — — piedfort	£50
1989 Scottish rev as 1984, silver, proof	£20

	BU
1989 — — piedfort	£40
1990 Welsh rev as 1985,	
silver, proof	£25
1991 Northern Ireland rev as 1986	
silver, proof	£25
1992 English rev as 1987	
silver, proof	£25
1993 Royal Coat of Arms (reverse as	
1983), silver proof	£30
1993 — — piedfort	£50
1994 Scottish Lion, silver, proof ...	£35
Ditto, Unc. in folder	£5
1994 — silver, piedfort	£50
1995 Welsh dragon, silver, proof	£25
Ditto, Unc in folder, English version ...	£5
1995 — silver, piedfort	£50
1996 Northern Ireland Celtic Ring	
Unc in folder	£5
Silver, proof	£27
Silver, piedfort	£50

Note that the edge inscriptions on £2 and £1 appear either upright or inverted in relation to the obverse. (Sovereign and half sovereign prices are not listed here but in the main listings under milled gold.)

FIFTY PENCE

1969	£1
1970	£1
1973 EEC	£1
1973 — proof	£3
1976–1981	f
1982 rev changed to FIFTY PENCE	
instead of NEW PENCE...	f
1983, 1985	f
1992 European Community	f
1992 — silver, proof	£30
1992 — silver, proof peidfort	£55
1992 — gold, proof	£400
1994 Normandy landing	f
1994 – silver, proof	£28
1994 – silver, piedfort	£50
1994 – gold, proof	£400

TWENTY-FIVE PENCE

1972 Silver Wedding	£1
1972 — Silver, proof...	£25
1977 Jubilee	£1
1977 — silver, proof	£20
1980 Queen Mother's 80th birthday ...	£1
1980 — in blister pack	£3
1980 — silver, proof	£32
1981 Royal Wedding	£1
1981 — in folder	£3
1981 — silver, proof	£30

TWENTY PENCE

1982	f
1982 silver, proof piedfort	£40
1983, 1984, 1985, 1987, 1988-1994	f

TEN PENCE

1968	£0.25
1969	£0.25
1970	£0.20
1971	£0.20
1973	£0.20
1974–1977, 1979–1981	f
1992 new size (24.5mm diameter),	
silver, proof, piedfort	£30

	BU
1992 old and new size,	
silver, proofs	£30
1992 — cu-ni	f

FIVE PENCE

1968-1971	*
1975, 1977-1980, 1987, 1988, 1989 ...	f
1990 silver, proof, old and new	£26
1990, 1991, 1992, 1994 – cu-ni	f

TWO PENCE

1971	*
1975-1981	f
1985 new portrait, rev changed to	
TWO PENCE instead of NEW PENCE ...	f
1986-1994	f

ONE PENNY

1971	*
1973–1981	f
1982 rev changed to ONE PENNY	
instead of NEW PENNY	f
1983, 1984	f
1985 new portrait	f
1986-1994	f

HALF PENNY

1971, ...	*
1973–1981	*
1982 rev changed to HALFPENNY	
instead of ½ NEW PENNY	*
1983	*

Proof and Specimen Sets

Proof or specimen sets have been issued since 1887 by the Royal Mint in official cases. Prior to that date, sets were issued privately by the engraver. Some sets are of currency coins, easily distinguishable from proofs which have a vastly superior finish. The two 1887 sets frequently come on to the market, hence their place in this list. The 1953 'plastic' set, though made up of currency coins, is official. It was issued in a plastic packet, hence the name. Apart from the sets stated, as being uncirculated, currency or specimen, all those in the following listing are proof sets.

GEORGE IV
	FDC
New issue, **1826**. Five pounds to farthing (11 coins) ...	**£16000**

WILLIAM IV
Coronation, **1831**. Two pounds to farthing (14 coins)...	**£12500**

VICTORIA
Young head, **1839**, 'Una and the Lion' five pounds plus sovereign to farthing (15 coins)	**£20000**
Young head, **1853**. Sovereign to quarter farthing, including 'Gothic' crown (16 coins)	**£15000**
Jubilee head, Golden Jubilee, **1887**. Five pounds to Threepence ('full sset' – 11 coins)	**£5000**
As above, currency set (unofficial)	**£1350**
Jubilee head, Golden Jubilee, **1887**. Crown to threepence ('short set' – 7 coins)	**£750**
As above, currency set (unofficial)	**£175**
Old head, **1893**. Five pounds to threepence ('full set') – 10 coins)	**£5500**
Old head, **1893**. Crown to threepence ('short set' – 6 coins)	**£900**

EDWARD VII
Coronation, **1902**. Five pounds to Maundy penny – matt proofs (13 coins)	**£1250**
Coronation, **1902**. Sovereign to Maundy penny – matt proofs (11 coins)	**£325**

GEORGE V
Coronation, **1911**. Five pounds to Maundy penny (12 coins)	**£2000**
Coronation, **1911**. Sovereign to Maundy penny (10 coins)	**£500**
Coronation**1911**, Halfcrown to Maundy penny (8 coins)	**£165**
New types. **1927**. Crown to threepence (6 coins)	**£125**

GEORGE VI
Coronation, **1937**. Gold set, five pounds to half sovereign (4 coins)	**£1300**
Coronation, **1937**. Silver and bronze set, crown to farthing including Maundy money (15 coins)	**£90**
Mid-century, **1950**. Halfcrown to farthing (9 coins)	**£40**
Festival of Britian, **1951**. Crown to farthing (10 coins)	**£50**

ELIZABETH II
Coronation, **1953**, Crown to farthing (10 coins)	**£35**
Coronation, **1953**, Currency ('plastic') set, official, halfcrown to farthing (9 coins)	**£10**
Specimen decimal set, **1968** 10p, 5p; **1971** 2p, 1p, ½p in wallet (5 coins)	**£1**
Last £sd coins, **1970** (sets issued 1971–73). Halfcrown to halfpenny (8 coins)	**£15**
Proof decimal set, **1971** (issued 1973), 50p, 10p, 5p, 2p, 1p, ½p	**£15**
Proof decimal set, **1972**. 50p, Silver Wedding, 25p, 10p, 5p, 2p, 1p, ½p....	**£15**
Proof decimal sets, **1973, 1974, 1975, 1976**. 50p to ½p (6 coins)	**£9**
Proof decimal set, **1977**. 50p to ½p, plus Jubilee crown (7 coins)	**£13**
Uncirculated decimal set, **1978**. 50p to ½p (6 coins)	**£1.50**
Proof decimal set, **1978**. 50p to ½p (6 coins)...	**£15**
Proof decimal set, **1979**. 50p to ½p (6 coins)...	**£15**
Proof decimal set, **1980**. 50p to ½p (6 coins)...	**£11**
Proof gold set, **1980**. Five pounds, two pounds, sovereign, half sovereign (4 coins)	**£600**
Commemorative proof coind set, **1981**. Five pounds, sovereign, Royal Wedding, silver crown, 50p to ½p (9 coins) ...	**£450**
Commemorative set, **1981**. Sovereign and Royal Wedding silver crown (2 coins)	**£110**
Proof decimal set, **1981**. 50p to ½p (6 coins) ...	**£11**
Proof gold set, **1982**. Five pounds, two pounds, sovereign, half sovereign (4 coins)...	**£600**
Proof decimal set, **1982**. 50p to ½p including 20p (7 coins)	**£14**
Uncirculated decimal set, **1982**. 50p to ½p including 20p (7 coins)	**£3.75**
Proof gold set, **1983**. Two pounds, sovereign, half sovereign (3 coins)...	**£300**
Proof decimal set, **1983**. £1 to ½p (8 coins)	**£20**
Uncirculated decimal set, **1983**. £1 to ½p (8 coins)	**£5**
Proof gold set, **1984**. Five pounds, sovereign, half sovereign (3 coins)...	**£475**
Proof decimal set, **1984**. £1 (Scottish rev) to ½p (8 coins)	**£15**
Uncirculated decimal set, **1984**. £1 (Scottish rev) to ½p (8 coins)	**£5**
Proof gold set, **1985**, new portrait. Five pounds, two pounds, sovereign, half sovereign (4 coins)...	**£600**
Proof decimal set, **1985**, new portrait. £1 (Welsh rev) to 1p (7 coins) in de luxe case...	**£20**
Proof decimal set, **1985**. As above, in standard case	**£15**
Uncirculated decimal set, **1985**. £1 (Welsh rev) to 1p (7 coins)...	**£5**
Proof gold set, **1986**. Commonwealth Games two pounds, sovereign, half sovereign (3 coins)	**£385**

	FDC
Proof decimal set, **1986**. Commonwealth Games £2, Northern Ireland £1, 50p to 1p (8 coins), de luxe case	£25
Proof decimal set, **1986**. As above, in standard case	£20
Uncirculated decimal set, **1986**. As above, in folder	£12
Proof gold Britannia set, **1987**. One ounce, half ounce, quarter ounce tenth ounce (4 coins)	£700
Proof gold Britannia set, **1987**. Quarter ounce, tenth ounce (2 coins)	£150
Proof gold set, **1987**. Two pounds, sovereign, half sovereign (3 coins)	£300
Proof decimal set, **1987**, £1 (English rev) to 1p (7 coins). in de luxe case	£23
Proof decimal set, **1987**. As above, in standard case	£18
Uncirculated decimal set. **1987**. As above, in folder	£10
Proof gold Britannia set, **1988**. One ounce, half ounce, quarter ounce, tenth ounce (4 coins)	£725
Proof gold Britannia set, **1988**. Quarter ounce, tenth ounce (2 coins)	£150
Proof gold set, **1988**. Two pounds, sovereign, half sovereign (3 coins)	£325
Proof decimal set, **1988**. £1 (Royal Arms rev) to 1p (7 coins), in de luxe case	£26
Proof decimal set, **1988**. As above, in standard case	£19
Uncirculated decimal set, **1988**. As above, in folder	£11
Proof gold Britannia set, **1989**. One ounce, half ounce, quarter ounce, tenth ounce (4 coins)	£725
Proof gold Britannia set, **1989**. Quarter ounce, tenth ounce (2 coins)	£150
Proof gold set, **1989**. 500th anniversary of the sovereign. Five poinds, two pounds, sovereign, half sovereign (4 coins)	£900
Proof gold set, **1989**. 500th anniversary of the sovereign. Two pounds, sovereign, half sovereign (3 coins)	£400
Proof decimal set, **1989**. Bill of Rights £2. Claim of Right £2, £1 (Scottish rev as 1984), 50p to 1p (9 coins) in de luxe case	£32
Proof decimal set, **1989**. As above, in standard case	£27
Proof silver **1989**. As above (2 coins)	£40
Proof silver piedfort **1989**. £2 as above (2 coins)	£80
Uncirculated **1989**. As above (2 coins) in folder	£10
Uncirculated decimal set, **1989**. £1 (Scottish rev as 1984) to 1p (7 coins)	£13
Proof gold set, **1990**. Five pounds, tgwo pounds, sovereign, half sovereign (4 coins)	£800
Proof gold set, **1990**. Two pounds, sovereign, half sovereign (3 coins)	£350
Proof silver set, **1990**. Five pence (23.59mm diam) and five pence (18mm diam, new size)	£24.30
Proof decimal set, **1990**. £1 (Welsh rev as 1985), 50p, 20p, 10p, large and small 5p, 2p, 1p (8 coins) in de luxe case	£30
Proof decimal set, **1990**. As above, in standard case	£25
Uncirculated decimal set, **1990**. £1 (Welsh rev as 1985) to 1p, including large and small 5p (8 coins)	£15
Proof gold Britannia set, **1990**	£775
Proof decimal set, **1991**. £1-1p in de luxe case	£30
Proof decimal set, **1991**. As above, in standard case	£25
Proof gold set, **1991**. Five pounds, two pounds, sovereign, half sovereign (4 coins)	£900
Proof gold set, **1991**. Two pounds, sovereign, half sovereign (3 coins)	£450
Uncirculated decimal set, **1991**	£12
Proof gold Britannia set, **1991**	£775
Proof, decimal set, **1992**. As above, in standard case	£28
Uncirculated decimal set, **1992**	£12
Proof gold Britannia set, **1992**	£800
Proof gold set, **1992**. Five pounds, double sovereign, sovereign, half sovereign (4 coins)	£950
Proof gold set, **1992**. Double sovereign, sovereign, half sovereign (3 coins)	£450
Proof gold set, **1993**. Five pounds, double sovereign, sovereign, half sovereign (4 coins)	£975
Proof gold set, **1993**. Double sovereign, sovereign, half sovereign (3 coins)	£500
Proof decimal set **1993**. 8 coins, de luxe case	£35
Uncirculated decimal set, **1993**. (With two 50p, no £5)	£12
Proof gold Britannia set, **1993**	£825
Proof decimal set, **1993**. (With £5)	£30
Proof gold Britannia set, **1994**	£875
Proof gold set, **1994**. Five pounds, double sovereign, sovereign, half sovereign (4 coins)	£1100
Proof gold set, **1994**. Double sovereign, sovereign, half sovereign (3 coins)	£625
Uncirculated decimal set, **1994**	£14
Proof decimal set, **1994**, deluxe case	£34
Proof decimal set **1994**, standard case	£28
Proof gold set **1994**. Five pounds, double sovereign, sovereign, half sovereign (4 coins)	£1175
Proof gold Britannia set, **1995**	£900
Proof gold set **1995**. Double sovereign, sovereign, half sovereign (3 coins)	£500
Uncirculated decimal set **1995**	£10
Proof decimal set **1995** deluxe case	£36
Proof decimal set **1995** standard case	£29
Proof gold Britannia set, **1996**	£1050
Proof gold set, **1996**. £5 etc. (4 coins)	£1175
Proof gold set, **1996**. £2 – ½ sovereign (3 coins)	£495
Proof silver decimal set, £1 to 1p, (7 coins)	£95
Uncirculated set, **1996**. £2 – 1p	£11
Proof decimal set, **1996**. (With £5), 9 coins, deluxe case	£38
Proof decimal set, **1996**. (With £5), standard case	£31

Scottish Coins

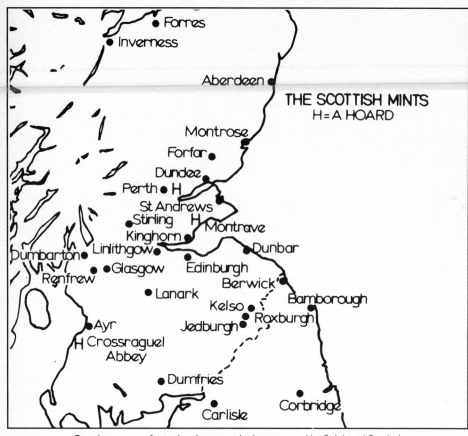

Based on a map of actual and supposed mints prepared by Spink and Son Ltd.

The number of mints which have been in operation in Scotland can be seen from the map above. The mints of the first coinage of Alexander III are the greatest number ever working together in Scotland, and it is this area that really attracts the collector of the different mint issues. For this reason, when we deal with this reign later on, we give a price for issues of each mint town, but not for any other reign.

MINT TOWN	KING(S)
ABERDEEN	Alexander III, David II Robert III, James I, II, III
AYR	Alexander III
BAMBOROUGH	Henry
BERWICK	David I, Malcolm IV, William I, Alexander II, III Robert Bruce, James III
CARLISLE	David I, Henry
CORBRIDGE	Henry
DUMBARTON	Robert III
DUMFRIES	Alexander III
DUNBAR	William I ?, Alexander III
DUNDEE	William I ?, Alexander III
DUNFERMLINE	William I
FORFAR	Alexander III
FORRES	Alexander III
GLASGOW	Alexander III
INVERNESS	Alexander III
JEDBURGH	Malcolm IV
KELSO	Alexander II
KINGHORN	Alexander III
LANARK	Alexander III
LINLITHGOW	James I, II
MONTROSE	Alexander III
PERTH	William I, Alexander III, Robert II to James II
RENFREW	Alexander III
ROXBURGH	Alexander III
ST ANDREWS	Alexander III
STIRLING	Alexander III, James I, II Mary Stuart

Prices are for the commonest coins in each case. Collectors should expect to pay these amounts and upwards. For further details see The Scottish Coinage, by I. Stewart (Spink, 1967, reprint 1975) and Standard Catalogue, Volume 2 (Seaby, 1984). Gold coins are indicated. All other coins are silver unless another metal is stated.

DAVID I 1124-53

	F	VF
Pennies	£450	£950

Four different groups; struck at the mints of Berwick, Carlisle, Roxburgh and Edinburgh

David I penny

HENRY 1136-52
(Earl of Huntingdon and Northumberland)

	F	VF
Pennies	£950	£3500

Three types; struck at the mints of Corbridge, Carlisle and Barnborough.

MALCOLM IV 1153-65

Pennies	£3500	£9000

Five types; struck at the mints of Roxburgh and Berwick.

WILLIAM THE LION 1165-1214

Pennies	£60	£140

Three issues; struck at the mints of Roxburgh, Berwick, Edinburgh, Dun (Dunfermline?), Perth

ALEXANDER II 1214-49

Pennies	£700	£1500

Mints of Berwick and Roxburgh, varieties of bust.

Alexander III penny

ALEXANDER III 1249-86
1st coinage pennies 1250-80
Mints

Mints		
Aberdeen	£90	£200
Ayr	£100	£250
Berwick	£40	£90
'DUN'	£125	£350
Edinburgh	£35	£100
Forfar	£120	£300
Fres	£120	£350
Glasgow	£150	£400
Inverness	£150	£400
Kinghorn	£150	£400
Lanark	£150	£400
Montrose	£250	*
Perth	£40	£120
Renfrew	£160	£400
Roxburgh	£35	£120
St. Andrews	£80	£200
Stirling	£100	£300
'TERWILANER' (uncertain name) ...	£150	*

2nd coinage c. 1280 —
Many types and varieties

	F	VF
Pennies	£15	£35
Halfpennies	£60	£170
Farthings	£150	£400

JOHN BALIOL 1292-6
1st coinage (rough surface issue)

Pennies	£90	£250
Halfpennies	£250	£550

2nd coinage (smooth surface issue)

Pennies	£120	£300
Halfpennies	£200	£450

Robert Bruce penny

ROBERT BRUCE 1306-29

Pennies	£250	£600
Halfpennies	£300	£750
Farthings		ext. rare

Probably all struck at Berwick.

David II groat

DAVID II 1329–71

Nobles (gold)		ext. rare
Groats	£70	£200
Halfgroats	£50	£150
Pennies	£40	£95
Halfpennies	£150	£350
Farthings	£500	*

Three issues, but these denominations were not struck for all issues. Edinburgh and Aberdeen mints.

ROBERT II 1371-90

Groats	£50	£170
Halfgroats	£70	£180
Pennies	£50	£130
Halfpennies	£130	£400

Some varieties. Struck at mints of Dundee, Edinburgh, Perth.

ROBERT II 1390-1406

Lions or crowns (gold)	£370	£750
Demy lions or halfcrowns (gold) ...	£350	£700
Groats	£60	£150
Halfgroats	£100	£300
Pennies	£150	£300
Halfpennies	£300	£700

Three issues, many varieties. Struck at mints of Edinburgh, Aberdeen, Perth, Dumbarton.

JAMES I 1406-37

Demies (gold)	£270	£500
Half demies (gold)	£375	£700
Groats	£100	£250

SCOTTISH COINS

	F	VF
Billon pennies	£60	*
Billon halfpennies	£100	*

Mints, Aberdeen, Edinburgh, Inverness, Linlithgow, Perth, Stirling.

JAMES II 1437-60

	F	VF
Demies (gold) from	£375	£750
Lions (gold) from...	£450	£1250
Half lions (gold) from		rare
Groats	£150	£500
Halfgroats	£350	£800
Billon pennies	£150	£400

Two issues, many varieties. Mints: Aberdeen, Edinburgh, Linlithgow, Perth, Roxburgh, Stirling.

ECCLESIASTICAL ISSUES C 1452-80

	F	VF
Bishop Kennedy copper pennies ...	£70	£150
Copper farthings	£150	*

Different types, varieties.

JAMES III 1460-88

	F	VF
Riders (gold) from	£650	£1500
Half riders (gold)	£800	£1600
Quarter riders (gold)	£750	£1800
Unicorns (gold)	£700	£1600
Groats ... ... from	£120	£300

James III groat and
James V one-third groat

	F	VF
Halfgroats from	£300	*
Pennies from	£80	£250
Billon placks from	£35	£90
Billon half placks from		very rare
Billon pennies from	£50	*
Copper farthings from...	£150	*

Many varieties. Mints: Edinburgh, Berwick, Aberdeen.

JAMES IV 1488-1513

	F	VF
Unicorns (gold)	£650	£1500
Half unicorns (gold)	£500	£1000
Lions or crowns (gold)	£700	£1600
Half lions (gold)	£1500	£3500
Pattern angel (gold)		unique
Groats	£260	£700
Halfgroats	£275	£600
Pennies [light coinage]	£350	*
Billon placks	£20	£70
Billon half placks	£80	£180
Billon pennies	£40	£95

Different types, varieties. Mint: Edinburgh only.

James V 'Bonnnet' piece of 1540

JAMES V 1513-42

	F	VF
Unicorns (gold)	£800	£1700
Half unicorns (gold)	£750	£1500
Crowns (gold)	£500	£1200
'Bonnet' pieces or ducats (gold) ...	£1300	£3000
Two-thirds ducats (gold)	£1800	£2500
One-third ducats (gold)	£2000	£3000
Groats from	£60	£150
One-third groats	£130	£300

James V groat

	F	VF
Billon placks	£20	£80
Billon bawbees	£15	£75
Billon half bawbees	£70	£150
Billon quarter bawbees		unique

Different issues, varieties. Edinburgh mint.

Note: from here on all Scottish coins were struck at Edinburgh.

MARY 1542-67
1st Period 1542-58

	F	VF
Crown (gold)	£750	£2000
Twenty shillings (gold)	£1700	*
Lions or forty-four shillings (gold) ...	£750	£1600

Lion or forty-four shillings of Mary

	F	VF
Half lions or twenty-two shillings (gold)	£475	£1350
Ryals or £3 pieces (gold)	£1750	£4000
Half ryals (gold)	£2700	*
Portrait testoons, 1553	£1000	£3500
Non-portrait testoons, 1555-8	£100	£375
— half testoons, 1555-8	£120	£350
Billon bawbees	£20	£75
– half bawbees	£50	£150
– pennies (facing bust)	£150	£450
– pennies (no bust) 1556	£100	£400
– lions, 1555, 1558	£20	£75
– placks, 1557	£20	£75

2nd period (Francis and Mary) 1558-60

	F	VF
Ducats or sixty shillings (gold)		ext. rare
Non-portrait testoons, 1558-61 ...	£150	£400
— half testoons, 1558-60	£150	£450
Twelvepenny groats [Nonsunt] 1558-9	£80	£200
— lions, 1559-60	£15	£70

3rd period (widowhood) 1560-5

Crown (gold) 1562 (Probably a pattern)		unique

Mary 3rd period testoon, 1562

	F	VF
Portrait testoons, 1561-2	£750	£2500
— half testoons, 1561-2	£850	*

4th period (Henry and Mary) 1565-7

| Portrait ryals, 1565 ... ... | ext. rare | |

The only available specimen was sold at
Glendining's in December 1990. It realised £48,000

| Non-portrait ryals, 1565-7 ... ... | £150 | £500 |

Mary and Henry non-portait ryal, 1565

— two-third ryals, 1565-7	£150	£550
— — undated	£350	£950
— one-third ryals, 1565-6	£150	£400
— testoons, 1565	ext. rare	

5th period (2nd widowhood) 1567

Non-portrait ryals, 1567	£140	£450
— two-thirds ryals, 1567	£150	£500
— one-third ryals, 1566-7	£170	£450

Mints: Edinburgh, Stirling (but only for some bawbees).

JAMES VI
Before English accession 1567-1603
1st coinage 1567-71

Ryals 1567-71	£140	£450
Two-third ryals —	£130	£400
One-third ryals —	£140	£450

2nd coinage 1571-80

Twenty pounds (gold)	£9500	£25000
Nobles, 1572-7, 1580	£80	£300
Half nobles —	£65	£200
Two merks, 1578-80	£950	*
Merks, 1579-80	£900	*

3rd coinage 1580-81

Ducats (gold), 1580	£3000	£6500
Sixteen shillings, 1581	£900	£3000
Eight shillings, 1581	£900	*
Four shillings, 1581	very rare	
Two shillings, 1581	ext. rare	

4th coinage 1582-88

Lion nobles (gold)	£2000	£5000
Two-third lion nobles (gold) ...	£2500	£6500
One-third lion nobles (gold) ...	£3000	£7500
Forty shillings, 1582	£2500	£7500
Thirty shillings, 1582-6	£180	£750
Twenty shillings, 1582-5	£130	£400
Ten shillings, 1582-4	£100	£250

James VI twenty shillings, 1582

5th coinage 1588

	F	VF
Thistle nobles (gold)	£1250	£3500

6th coinage 1591-93

Hat pieces (gold)	£2750	£6500
Balance half merks, 1591-3	£150	£400
Balance quarter merks, 1591	£250	£600

James VI gold rider, 1594

7th coinage, 1594-1601

Riders (gold)	£400	£900
Half riders (gold)	£300	£700
Ten shillings, 1593-5, 1598-1601	£80	£250
Five shillings, 1593-5, 1598-1601 ...	£90	£200
Thirty pennies, 1595-6, 1598-9, 1601	£75	£180
Twelve pennies, 1594-6	£60	£150

8th coinage 1601-4

Sword and sceptre pieces (gold) ...	£275	£600
Half sword and sceptre pieces (gold)	£220	£400
Thistle-merks, 1601-4	£40	£150
Half thistle merks —	£35	£120
Quarter thistle-merks —	£35	£100
Eighth thistle-merks, 1601-3 ...	£35	£150

Billon and copper issues

Billon placks or eightpenny groats ...	£20	£75
Billon half placks	£90	*
Billon hardheads	£25	£80
Billon saltire placks	£100	*
Copper twopence 1597	very rare	
Copper penny 1597	very rare	

After English accession 1603-25

Units (gold)	£400	£800
Double crowns (gold)	£450	£1200
Britain crowns (gold)	£350	*
Halfcrowns (gold)	£300	*
Thistle crowns (gold)	£250	*
Sixty shillings	£250	£700
Thirty shillings	£65	£200
Twelve shillings	£70	£170
Six Shillings	£100	*
Two Shillings	£50	*
One Shilling	£60	*

SCOTTISH COINS

James VI Gold Unit
(after English accession)

	F	VF
Sixpences	*	*
Copper twopences	£10	£50
Copper pennies	£20	£60

Charles I
Scottish
unit by
Briot

CHARLES I 1625-49
1st coinage 1625-36

	F	VF
Units (gold)	£450	£900
Double crowns (gold)...	£950	*
Britain crowns (gold)	ext. rare	
Sixty shillings	£275	£800
Thirty shillings	£60	£200
Twelve shillings	£60	£175
Six shillings...	very rare	
Two shillings...	£70	*
One shillings...	ext. rare	

2nd coinage 1636

	F	VF
Half merks ... ...:. ...	£35	£150
Forty penny pieces	£40	£100
Twenty penny pieces	£40	*

3rd coinage 1637-42

	F	VF
Units (gold)	£450	£1000
Half units (gold)	£600	*
Britain crowns (gold)	£400	£950
Britain half crowns (gold)	£200	£650
Sixty shillings	£300	£800
Thirty shillings	£50	£150
Twelve shillings	£50	£150
Six shillings	£50	£140
Half merks	£50	£150
Forty pennies	£20	£70
Twenty pennies	£12	£30
Three shillings	£40	£90
Two shillings	£40	£100
Copper twopences (lion)	£10	£50
— pennies —		rare
— twopences (CR crowned)	£10	£50
— twopences (Stirling turners) ...	£10	£40

CHARLES II 1660-85
1st coinage
Four merks

				F	VF
1664 thistle above bust	...	...	...	£200	*
1664 thistle below bust	...	...	...	£250	*
1665	...	...	...	...	*	*
1670	...	...	...	...	£170	*
1673	...	...	...	...	£175	*
1674 F below bust	...	...	...	£350	*
1675	...	...	...	...	£150	£450

Two merks

				F	VF
1664 thistle above bust	...	...	...	£175	£500

Charles II two merks, 1664
(thistle above bust)

				F	VF
1664 thistle below bust	...	...	...	£160	*
1670	...	...	...	...	£120	£450
1673	...	...	...	...	£120	£450
1673 F below bust	...	...	...	£200	*
1674	...	...	...	...	£250	*
1674 F below bust	...	...	...	£200	*
1675	...	...	...	...	£150	£450

Merks

				F	VF
1664	...	...	...	...	£35	£150
1665	...	...	...	...	£35	£150
1666	...	...	...	...	£75	*
1668	...	...	...	...	£40	£150
1669	...	...	...	...	£40	£150
1670	...	...	...	...	£35	£150
1671	...	...	...	...	£30	£130
1672	...	...	...	...	£30	£120
1673	...	...	...	...	£30	£140
1674	...	...	...	...	£50	£200
1674 F Below bust	...	...	...	£50	£200
1675 F below bust	...	...	...	£50	£200
1675	...	...	...	...	£95	£250

Half merks

				F	VF
1664	...	...	...	...	£50	£150
1665	...	...	...	...	£50	£150
1666	...	...	...	...	£75	£190
1667	...	...	...	...	£50	£150
1668	...	...	...	...	£50	£150
1669	...	...	...	...	£75	£190
1670	...	...	...	...	*	*
1671	...	...	...	...	£40	£150
1672	...	...	...	...	£40	£140
1673	...	...	...	...	£40	£150
1675 F below bust	...	...	...	£35	£150
1675	...	...	...	...	£45	£160

2nd coinage
Dollars

				F	VF
1676	...	...	...	...	£170	£450
1679	...	...	...	...	£170	£400
1680	...	...	...	...	£250	*
1681	...	...	...	...	£120	£350
1682	...	...	...	...	£120	£300

Half dollars

				F	VF
1675	...	...	...	...	£150	£400
1676	...	...	...	...	£170	£450
1681	...	...	...	...	...	£70	£400

Quarter dollars							F	VF
1675	...	...	...	...	...	...	£50	£200
1676	...	...	...	...	...	...	£50	£200
1677	...	...	...	...	...	...	£75	*
1678	...	...	...	...	...	...	£50	£200
1679	...	...	...	...	...	...	£75	*
1680	...	...	...	...	...	...	£50	£200
1681	...	...	...	...	...	...	£75	*
1682	...	...	...	...	...	...	£50	£200

Eighth dollars								
1676	...	...	...	...	...	...	£60	*
1677	...	...	...	...	...	...	£50	£150
1678/7	...	...	...	...	...	...	*	*
1679	...	...	...	...	...	...	*	*
1680	...	...	...	...	...	...	£75	£150
1682	...	...	...	...	...	...	£100	*

Sixteenth dollars								
1677	...	...	...	...	...	...	£35	£100
1678/7	...	...	...	...	...	...	£100	*
1679/7	...	...	...	...	...	...	£100	*
1680	...	...	...	...	...	...	£100	*
1681	...	...	...	...	...	...	£35	£100

Copper twopences CR[II]								
crowned	...	...	...	...	...	...	£20	£90
Copper bawbees, 1677-9	...	...					£35	£100
Copper turners, 1677-9	...	...					£20	£90

JAMES VII 1685-9

							F	VF
Sixty shillings 1688 proof only[1]							FDC	£950
— — gold proof only[1]							FDC	*

([1]Struck in 1828, not contemporary)
NB: A gold sixty shillings, 1688 realised £13,000 in the Beresford Jones collection sold by Spink, March 7, 1995.

Forty shillings								
1887	...	...	...	...	...	...	£80	£300
1688	...	...	...	...	...	...	£150	£400

Ten shillings								
1687	...	...	...	...	...	...	£90	£300
1688	...	...	...	...	...	...	£100	£320

James VII ten shillings, 1687

WILLIAM AND MARY 1689-94

Sixty shillings								
1691...	...	...	...	...	...	...	£150	£500
1692...	...	...	...	...	...	...	£100	£400

Forty shillings								
1989	...	...	...	...	...	...	£95	£300
1690	...	...	...	...	...	...	£90	£280
1691	...	...	...	...	...	...	£70	£270
1692	...	...	...	...	...	...	£90	£280
1693	...	...	...	...	...	...	£100	*
1694	...	...	...	...	...	...	£100	*

Twenty shillings								
1693	...	...	...	...	...	...	£90	£280
1694	...	...	...	...	...	...	£200	*

Ten shillings								
1689	...	...	...	...	...	...	*	*
1690	...	...	...	...	...	...	£100	£250
1691	...	...	...	...	...	...	£70	£200
1692	...	...	...	...	...	...	£40	£120
1694	...	...	...	...	...	...	£150	£400

SCOTTISH COINS

William and Mary 1694 five shillings

Five shillings							F	VF
1691	...	...	...	...	...	...	£70	£250
1694	...	...	...	...	...	...	£60	£200
Copper bawbee 1691-4			...	...			£40	£100
Copper bodle 1691-4	...		...	...			£30	£75

WILLIAM II 1694-1702

Pistole (gold) 1701	...	...	...	...	£1500	£3000
Half pistole (gold) 1701	...	...	...	£1250	£3000

Sixty shillings								
1699...	...	...	...	...	...	...	*	*

Forty shillings								
1695	...	...	...	...	...	...	£70	£300
1696	...	...	...	...	...	...	£50	£200
1697	...	...	...	...	...	...	£75	£300
1698	...	...	...	...	...	...	£60	£200
1699	...	...	...	...	...	...	£100	*
1700	...	...	...	...	...	...	£200	*

Twenty shillings								
1695	...	...	...	...	...	...	£50	£150
1696	...	...	...	...	...	...	£50	£150
1697	...	...	...	...	...	...	*	*
1698	...	...	...	...	...	...	£80	£250
1699	...	...	...	...	...	...	*	*

Ten shillings								
1695	...	...	...	...	...	...	£75	*
1696	...	...	...	...	...	...	£70	£200
1697	...	...	...	...	...	...	£70	*
1698	...	...	...	...	...	...	£70	*
1699	...	...	...	...	...	...	£100	£350

Five shillings								
1695	...	...	...	...	...	...	£50	*
1696	...	...	...	...	...	...	£50	*
1697	...	...	...	...	...	...	£20	£100
1699	...	...	...	...	...	...	£40	*
1700	...	...	...	...	...	...	£40	*
1701	...	...	...	...	...	...	£50	*
1702	...	...	...	...	...	...	£60	£200
Copper bawbee 1695-7	...	...	...				£20	£100
Copper bodle 1695-7	...	...	...				£25	£120

ANNE 1702-14
Pre-Union 1702-7

Ten shillings								
1705	...	...	...	...	...	...	£50	£150
1706	...	...	...	...	...	...	£100	£300

Five shillings								
1705	...	...	...	...	...	...	£15	£50
1706	...	...	...	...	...	...	£20	£80

Post-Union 1707-14
see under British milled series

JAMES VIII 1688-1766 (The Old Pretender)

Guinea 1716, gold	...	...	...	...	FDC	£3000
— — silver	...	...	...	...	FDC	£800
— — bronze	...	...	...	...	FDC	£1200
Crown 1709	...	...	...	...		unique
Crown 1716, silver	...	...	...	...	FDC	£900
— — gold	...	...	...	...		ext. rare
— — bronze	...	...	...	...		ext. rare
— — white metal...	...	...	...	...		ext. rare

N.B. All the 1716-dated pieces were struck in 1828 from original dies.

Irish Coins

Hammered Issues
995-1661

Prices are for the commonest coins in each case. It should be remembered that most of the Irish coins of these times are in fairly poor condition and it is difficult to find specimens in VF condition upwards. For more details see The Guide Book to the Coinage of Ireland AD 995 to the present day, *by Anthony Dowle and Patrick Finn (ref. DF in following lists); Seaby's* Coins of Scotland, Ireland and the Islands, *which is* Volume Two of Seaby's Standard Catalogue *(ref Sby in price list); and also Patrick Finn's* Irish Coin Values.

All coins are silver unless otherwise stated.

HIBERNO-NORSEMEN OF

DUBLIN 995-1150	F	VF
Pennies, imitative of English coins, many types and varieties ... from	£90	£150

Hiberno-Norse penny, c 1015-1035

JOHN, as Lord of Ireland
c1185-1199

Halfpennies, with profile portrait	extremely rare	
Halfpennies, with facing head	£40	£80
Farthings	£200	£450

Different types, varieties, mints, moneyers.

JOHN DE COURCY
Lord of Ulster 1177-1205

Halfpennies	very rare	
Farthings	£350	£750

Different types, varieties, mints, moneyers.

Triangle type penny of King John

JOHN as King of England and
Lord of Ireland c 1199-1216
Rex/Triangle types

Pennies ... ...from	£40	£90
Halfpennies	£50	£120
Farthings	£175	£400

Different varieties, mints and moneyers.

HENRY III 1216-1272

Pennies (c 1251-1254) ... ...from	£35	£95

Dublin only, moneyers DAVI and RICARD. Many varieties.

Edward I Waterford penny

EDWARD I 1272-1307		F	VF
Pennies ... ...from		£20	£50
Halfpennies		£60	£150
Farthings		£130	£300

Dublin, Waterford and Cork. Many different issues.

EDWARD III 1327-1377

Halfpennies, Dublin mint		ext. rare

There were no Irish coins struck for Edward II, Richard II, Henry IV or Henry V.

HENRY VI 1422-1461

Pennies, Dublin mint		ext. rare

Edward IV untitled crown groat

EDWARD IV 1461-1483		F	VF
Untitled crown groats ... ...from		£250	£500
— pennies		£475	*
Titled crown groats		£850	*
— halfgroats		ext. rare	
— pennies		very rare	
Cross on rose/sun groats		£500	*
—— pennies		£400	*
Bust/rose-sun double groats		£1400	£3500
—— groats		£1750	*
—— halfgroats		ext. rare	
—— pennies		ext. rare	
'English style' groats		£45	£150
— halfgroats		£200	£375
— pennies		£45	£120
— halfpennies		ext. rare	
Bust/rose-cross groats		£350	£750
—— pennies		£75	£150
copper issues			
Crown/cross farthing		£800	*
—— half farthing		£500	*
PATRICIUS/SALVATOR			
Farthing		£450	£950
3 crowns/sun half-farthing		very rare	

This is, of course, a very abbreviated listing of the issues of Edward IV which are numerous and complicated, and still pose numismatists many problems. There are also many varieties and different mints.

IRISH COINS

RICHARD III 1483-1485

	F	VF
Bust/rose-cross groats ... ...from	**£500**	**£1250**
—— halfgroat		unique
—— penny		unique
Cross and Pellet Penny	**£500**	*
Three-crown groats	**£350**	**£750**

Different mints, varieties, etc.

HENRY VII 1485-1509

Early issues

Three-crown groats ... ... from	**£50**	**£150**
— halfgroats	**£125**	**£275**
— pennies	**£300**	**£650**
— halfpennies		ext. rare

Different mints, varieties, etc.

LAMBERT SIMNEL (pretender) 1487

Three-crown groats	**£950**	**£2500**

Different mints, varieties.

HENRY VII 1485-1509

Later issues

Facing bust groats	**£70**	**£150**
— halfgroats	**£450**	*
— pennies		very rare
Crowned H pennies		very rare

Many varieties. Mainly Dublin. Waterford is extremely rare.

Henry VIII 'harp groat, initials HA

HENRY VIII 1509-1547

'Harp' groats	**£30**	**£90**
— halfgroat	**£250**	**£550**

These harp coins carry crowned initials, e.g., HA (Henry and Anne Boleyn), HI (Henry and Jane Seymour), HK (Henry and Katherine Howard), HR (Henricus Rex).

Henry VIII portrait groat

Posthumous issues

Portrait groats	**£50**	**£150**
— halfgroats	**£65**	**£200**
— pennies	**£150**	**£300**
— halfpennies	**£250**	*

Different busts, mintmarks etc.

EDWARD VI 1547-15553

Base shillings 1552 (MDLII)	**£400**	**£950**
— contemporary copy	**£40**	**£150**

Mary 1553 shilling

MARY 1553-1558

	F	VF
Shillings 1553 (MDLIII)	**£400**	**£1000**
Shillings 1554 (MDLIIII)		ext. rare
Groats		very rare
Halfgroats		ext. rare
Pennies		ext. rare

Several varieties of the shillings and groats.

PHILIP AND MARY 1554-1558

Base shillings	**£140**	**£375**
— groats	**£45**	**£130**

Several minor varieties.

ELIZABETH I 1558-1603

Base portrait shillings	**£130**	**£475**
— groats	**£90**	**£350**

Elizabeth I 1561 shilling

Fine portrait shillings 1561	**£95**	**£375**
— groats —	**£200**	**£550**
Base shillings arms-harp	**£80**	**£300**
— sixpences ——	**£75**	**£150**
— threepences ——	**£130**	**£375**
— pennies ——	**£12**	**£70**
— halfpennies ——	**£35**	**£140**

JAMES I 1603-1625

Shillings	**£40**	**£150**
— Sixpences	**£30**	**£100**

Different issues, busts and mintmarks.

CHARLES I 1625-1649

Seige money of the Irish Rebellion 1642-1649

Siege coins are rather irregular in size and shape.

Kilkenny Money 1642

Copper halfpennies (**F**)	**£150**	**£350**
Copper farthings (**F**)	**£150**	**£400**

Inchiquin Money 1642-1646
(The only gold coins struck in Ireland. Of the very few known specimens there is only one privately owned; the others are in museums.)

Gold double pistoles		ext. rare
Gold pistoles (**F**)		ext. rare
Crowns	**£750**	**£1500**

Inchiquin shilling

Youghal farthing

	F	VF
Halfcrowns	£1000	*
Shillings	£1600	*
Ninepences	£1800	*
Sixpences	£1400	*
Groats (F)	£1400	*
Threepences	£1500	*

Three issues and many varieties.

Ormonde Money 1643		
Crowns (F)	£220	£550
Halfcrowns (F)	£170	£400
Shillings	£65	£150

Ormonde sixpence

Sixpences (F)	£50	£150
Groats (F)	£45	£140
Threepences	£35	£80
Halfgroats (F)	£220	£475

Many varieties.

Rebel Money 1643		
Crowns	£1500	*
Halfcrowns	£1750	*

Town Pieces 1645-1647		
Bandon		
Copper farthings (F)	£100	*

Kinsale copper farthing

Kinsale		
Copper farthings (F)	£90	*

Youghal		
Copper farthings (F)	£100	£750
Brass twopences		ext. rare
Pewter threepences		ext. rare

Cork		
Shillings (F)	£950	*
Sixpences (F)	£500	£1000
Copper halfpennies		ext. rare
Copper farthings	£80	*
Elizabeth I shillings countermarked		
CORKE (F)		ext. rare

	F	VF
Dublin Money 1649		
Crowns	£1250	£2500
Halfcrowns	£1400	£3000

CHARLES II 1660-1685
Armstrong issues 1660-1661

Copper farthings	£45	£300

Charles II to George IV

This series, of which all the issues except Bank of Ireland tokens were struck in base metal, features a large number of varieties, many of which are unpublished, but there is space here for only the main types and best-known variants. A number of rare proofs have also been omitted.

Except for the 'gunmoney' of James II, Irish copper coins are notably hard to find in the top grades, especially the so-called 'Voce populi' issues and specimens of Wood's coinage (which are reasonably common in the lower grades, apart from the rarities).

in only three grades — Fair, Fine and VF. The majority of these hastily produced coins were not well struck and many pieces with little substantial wear are, arguably, not EF in the strictest sense.

Finally, a note on the dating of gunmoney. In the calendar used up to 1723 the legal or civil year commenced on March 25 in Great Britain and Ireland, so December 1689 came before, not after January, February and March 1689. Coins dated March 1689 and March 1690 were struck in the same month.

CHARLES II	Fair	F	VF	EF
St Patrick's coinage				
Halfpenny	£50	£120	*	*
— star in rev legend	£60	£150	*	*
Farthing	£30	£80	£250	*
— stars in rev legend	£35	£80	£300	*
— cloud around				
St Patrick	*	*	*	*
— martlet below king	*	*	*	*
— annulet below king	*	*	*	*

St Patrick's farthing

IRISH COINS

Regal coinage	Fair	F	VF	EF
Halfpennies				
1680 large letters				
small cross	£25	£60	£130	*
1680 large letters,				
pellets	£5	£25	£100	£250
1681 large letters ...	£5	£25	£100	£250
1681 small letters ...	*	*	*	*
1682 large letters ...	*	*	*	*
1682 small letters ...	£6	£15	£100	£250
1683	£5	£12	£100	£250
1684	£12	£35	£150	*

JAMES II
Regular coinage
Halfpennies				
1685...	£1	£10	£100	£250
1686	£1	£10	£100	£250
1687	*	*	*	*
1688	£10	£35	£180	*

Emergency coinage
Gunmoney
Crowns				
1690	£6	£30	£100	*
1690 'chubby'				
horseman, sword				
to E (Sby 6577) ...	£10	£60	£200	*
1690 similar (DF 373)	£10	£45	£180	*

James II gunmoney crown

Large halfcrowns				
1689 July	£2	£20	£70	*
1689 August ...	£1.25	£15	£45	*
1689 September ...	£1	£15	£45	*
1689 October	£1	£15	£45	*
1689 November ...	£1	£15	£45	*
1689 December ...	£1	£15	£45	*
1689 January	£1	£15	£50	*
1689 February	£1	£15	£45	*
1689 March ...	£1	£15	£45	*
1690 March	£1	£15	£45	*
1690 April	£2	£15	£60	*
1690 May	£2	£15	£60	*
Small halfcrowns				
1690 April	*	*	*	*
1690 May	£1	£12	£45	*
1690 June	£1	£12	£45	*
1690 July	£1	£12	£45	*
1690 August	£2	£15	£50	*
1690 September ...	*	*	*	*
1690 October	£70	*	*	*
Large shillings				
1689 July	£1	£10	£40	£120
1689 August	£0.85	£8	£40	£100
1689 September ...	£0.85	£8	£35	£100
1689 April	£0.85	£8	£35	£100

	Fair	F	VF	EF
1689 November ...	£1	£8	£40	£100
1689 December ...	£1	£6	£40	£100
1689 January	£1	£6	£40	£100
1689 February ...	£1	£6	£40	£100
1689 March	£1	£6	£40	£100
1690 March	£1	£6	£40	£100
1690 April	£1	£6	£40	£100
Small shillings				
1690 April	£1	£6	£30	£100
1690 May	£1	£6	£30	£100
1690 June	£1	£6	£30	£100

Gunmoney small shilling, June 1690

	Fair	F	VF	EF
1690 July	*	*	*	*
1690 August	*	*	*	*
1690 September ...	*	*	*	*
Sixpences				
1689 June	£1	£6	£35	£95
1689 July	£1	£6	£35	£95
1689 August	£1	£6	£35	£95
1689 September ...	£1	£6	£35	£95
1689 October	*	*	*	*
1689 November ...	£1	£6	£35	£95
1689 December ...	£1	£6	£35	£95
1689 January	£1	£6	£35	£95
1689 February ...	£4	£10	£45	£110
1689 March	*	*	*	*
1690 March	*	*	*	*
1690 April	*	*	*	*
1690 May	£12	£20	£90	*
1690 June	*	*	*	*
1690 October	*	*	*	*

Pewter Money				
Crown	£190	£350	£1000	*
Groat	£95	£220	£700	*
Penny large bust ...	£100	£200	£500	*
Penny small bust ...	£100	£200	£500	*
Halfpenny large bust	£50	£100	£250	*
Halfpenny small bust	£50	£120	£350	*

Limerick Money halfpenny

Limerick Money				
Halfpenny	£8	£40	£95	*
Farthing reversed N	£10	£50	£100	*
— normal N	£15	£55	£120	*

WILLIAM AND MARY
Halfpennies				
1692	£2	£15	£90	*
1693	£2	£25	£100	*
1694	£2	£20	£90	*

	Fair	F	VF	EF
WILLIAM III				
Halfpenny draped bust	£10	£25	£120	*
Halfpenny crude undraped bust	£25	£100	*	*
GEORGE I				
Wood's coinage				
Halfpennies				
1722 harp left	£15	£70	£200	*
1722 harp right	£3	£12	£100	£350
1723	£2	£8	£80	£250
1723 obv Rs altered Bs	£2	£8	£80	£250
1723 no stop after date	£2	£8	£80	£250
1723/2	£6	£20	£100	*
1723 star in rev legend	*	*	*	*
1723 no stop before HIBERNIA	£4	£10	£100	£250
1724 head divides rev legend	£4	£10	£100	£220
1724 legend continuous over head	£5	£15	£140	£350

George I Wood's farthing, 1723

Farthings				
1722 harp left	£20	£70	£350	£600
1723 D:G:	£10	£30	£120	£400
1723 DEI GRATIA ...	£4	£10	£90	£300
1724	£5	£25	£140	£350

GEORGE II				
Halfpennies				
1736	*	£3	£35	£150
1737	*	£2	£35	£150
1738	*	£3	£30	£120
1741	*	£3	£30	£120
1742	*	£3	£30	£120
1743	*	£5	£35	£120
1744	*	£3	£30	£120
1744/3	*	£3	£30	£120
1746	*	£3	£30	£120
1747	*	£3	£30	£120
1748	*	£3	£30	£120
1749	*	£3	£30	£120
1750	*	£3	£30	£120
1751	*	£3	£30	£120
1752	*	£3	£30	£120
1753	*	£3	£30	£120
1755	*	£8	£70	£200
1760	*	£2	£35	£120
Farthings				
1737	*	£2	£40	£100
1738	*	£1	£30	£90
1744	*	£4	£40	£100
1760	*	£4	£40	£100

GEORGE III				
Voce populi coinage				
Halfpennies (1760)				
Type 1 (DF 565)	£16	£40	£120	£250

1760 voce populi halfpenny

	Fair	F	VF	EF
Type 2 (DF 566)	£12	£35	£160	*
Type 3 (DF 567)	£14	£45	£170	*
Type 4 (DF 569)	£12	£40	£170	*
Type 5 (DF 570)	£12	£40	£170	*
Type 6 (DF 571)	£12	£50	£170	*
Type 7 (DF 572)	£12	£40	£170	*
Type 8 (DF 573)	£12	£40	£170	*
Type 9 (DF 575)	£14	£50	£170	*
Type 9, P before head (DF 576)	£14	£50	£170	*
Type 9, P under head (DF 577)	£14	£50	£170	*
Farthings (1760)				
Type 1 loop to truncation	£45	£100	£350	£750
Type 2 no loop	*	*	*	*
London coinage				
Halfpennies				
1766	*	£2	£30	£120
1769	*	£2	£30	£120
1769 2nd type	*	£2.50	£30	£120
1775	*	£2	£30	£120
1776	*	*	*	*
1781	*	£3	£30	£120
1782	*	£3	£30	£120
Soho coinage				
Penny 1805	*	£3	£30	£140
Halfpenny 1805 ...	*	£3	£30	£120
Farthing 1806	*	£1	£25	£100
Bank of Ireland token coinage				
Six shillings 1804 ...	£10	£45	£275	£900

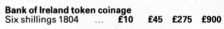

1804 six shilling Bank of Ireland token

Thirty pence 1808 ...	£2	£10	£50	£200
Ten pence 1805 ...	£1	£8	£30	£100

	Fair	F	VF	EF
Ten pence 1806 ...	£1	£6	£30	£70
Ten pence 1813 ...	£1	£5	£20	£60

Bank of Ireland ten pence token, 1813

	Fair	F	VF	EF
Five pence 1805 ...	£1	£5	£15	£50
Five pence 1806 ...	£2	£8	£25	£75

GEORGE IV

	Fair	F	VF	EF
Penny 1822	*	£3	£30	£140
Penny 1823 ...	*	£3	£30	£140
Halfpenny 1822 ...	*	£2	£25	£120
Halfpenny 1823 ...	*	£2	£25	£120

Free State and Republic

Proofs exist for nearly all dates of the modern Irish coinage. However, only a few dates have become available to collectors or dealers and, apart from the 1928 proofs, are all at least very rare. They have therefore been omitted from this list.

TEN SHILLINGS

	F	VF	EF	Unc
1966	*	£2.50	£5	£7.50
1966	*	*	*	£15

HALFCROWNS

	F	VF	EF	Unc
1928	£3	£6	£12	£25
1928 proof	*	*	*	£40

Reverse of halfcrown

	F	VF	EF	Unc
1930	£3	£10	£75	£150
1931	£6	£20	£85	£200
1933	£3	£15	£75	£125
1934	£3	£15	£35	£100
1937	£30	£75	£200	£500
1939	£3	£6	£10	£20
1940	£3	£5	£10	£25
1941	£4	£6	£15	£30
1942	£4	£6	£15	£25
1943	£70	£150	£600	£1500
1951	*	£1	£5	£25
1954	*	£1	£5	£25
1955	*	£1	£5	£15
1959	*	£1	£5	£10
1961	*	£1	£5	£12

	F	VF	EF	Unc
1961 mule (normal) obv/pre-1939 rev)	£5	£12	£200	*
1962	*	*	*	£5
1963	*	*	*	£5
1964	*	*	*	£5
1966	*	*	*	£3
1967	*	*	*	£3

FLORINS

	F	VF	EF	Unc
1928	£2	£4	£8	£20
1928 proof	*	*	*	£30
1930	£3	£6	£30	£150
1931	£3	£10	£60	£150
1933	£3	£10	£50	£125
1934	£10	£25	£75	£300
1935	£3	£10	£30	£150
1937	£3	£15	£50	£125
1939	£2	£4	£10	£20
1940	£2	£5	£12	£20
1941	£2	£5	£12	£30
1942	£2	£5	£12	£30
1943	£1500	£3000	£6000	£10000
1951	*	*	£3	£10
1954	*	*	£3	£10
1955	*	*	£3	£10
1959	*	*	£3	£10
1961	*	£3	£6	£20
1962	*	*	£3	£10
1963	*	*	£3	£10
1964	*	*	*	£3
1965	*	*	*	£3
1966	*	*	*	£3
1968	*	*	*	£3

SHILLINGS

	F	VF	EF	Unc
1928	*	£3	£8	£12
1928 proof	*	*	*	£25
1930	£2	£10	£50	£150
1931	£2	£10	£50	£150
1933	£3	£10	£50	£150
1935	£2	£5	£20	£50
1937	£5	£25	£150	£200
1939	*	£3	£6	£15
1940	*	£3	£8	£20
1941	£2	£5	£8	£20
1942	£2	£5	£8	£20
1951	*	£1	£3	£10
1954	*	*	£3	£10
1955	*	£2	£5	£15
1959	*	*	£3	£10
1962	*	*	*	£3
1963	*	*	*	£2
1964	*	*	*	£3
1966	*	*	*	£2
1968	*	*	*	£2

1968 shilling

SIXPENCES

	F	VF	EF	Unc
1928	*	£1	£3	£10
1928 proof	*	*	*	£20
1934	*	£1	£8	£30
1935	*	£3	£12	£50
1939	*	£1	£5	£20

	F	VF	EF	Unc
1940	*	£1	£5	£20
1942	*	*	£5	£20
1945	*	£5	£25	£50
1946	£1	£5	£50	£100
1947	*	£2	£20	£50
1948	*	£2	£8	£25
1949	*	*	£5	£25
1950	*	£2	£15	£50
1952	*	£1	£4	£15
1953	*	£1	£4	£15
1955	*	£1	£4	£15
1956	*	*	£3	£10
1958	*	£1	£5	£25
1959	*	*	£2	£6
1960	*	*	£2	£6
1961	*	*	£2	£6
1962	*	*	£3	£30
1963	*	*	*	£3
1964	*	*	*	£3
1966	*	*	*	£3
1967	*	*	*	£3

1968 sixpence

	F	VF	EF	Unc
1968	*	*	*	£2
1969	*	*	*	£3

THREEPENCES

	F	VF	EF	Unc
1928	*	£1	£3	£8
1928 proof	*	*	*	£12
1933	£1	£3	£20	£100
1934	*	£1	£5	£20
1935	£1	£3	£15	£50
1939	£1	£5	£50	£150
1940	*	*	£5	£25
1942	*	*	£5	£20
1943	*	*	£5	£20
1946	*	*	£5	£15
1948	*	£2	£15	£50
1949	*	*	£5	£20
1950	*	*	£2	£6
1953	*	*	£2	£5
1956	*	*	£1	£4
1961	*	*	*	£3
1962	*	*	*	£3
1963	*	*	*	£3
1964	*	*	*	£3
1965	*	*	*	£3
1966	*	*	*	£3

1967 threepence

	F	VF	EF	Unc
1967	*	*	*	*
1968	*	*	*	*

PENNIES

	F	VF	EF	Unc
1928	*	*	£3	£10
1928 proof	*	*	*	£30
1931	*	£2	£10	£30

	F	VF	EF	Unc
1933	*	£3	£10	£40
1935	*	*	£6	£20
1937	*	*	£9	£30
1938 (unique?)	*	*	*	*
1940	£2	£6	£50	*
1941	*	£1	£6	£15
1942	*	*	£3	£10
1943	*	*	£5	£15
1946	*	*	£3	£10
1948	*	*	£3	£10
1949	*	*	£3	£10
1950	*	*	£3	£10
1952	*	*	£2	£5
1962	*	*	£2	£4
1963	*	*	*	£2
1964	*	*	*	£2
1965	*	*	*	£1
1966	*	*	*	£1
1967	*	*	*	£1
1968	*	*	*	£1

HALFPENNIES

	F	VF	EF	Unc
1928	*	£3	£6	£20
1928 proof	*	*	*	£20
1933	£1	£5	£25	£75
1935	*	£5	£15	£50
1937	*	*	£4	£8
1939	£4	£10	£25	£60
1940	*	£3	£20	£35
1941	*	*	£5	£10
1942	*	*	£2	£10
1943	*	*	£3	£10
1946	*	*	£5	£20
1949	*	*	£3	£5
1953	*	*	*	£3
1964	*	*	*	£1.50
1965	*	*	*	£1.50
1966	*	*	*	£1.50
1967	*	*	*	£1.50

FARTHINGS

	F	VF	EF	Unc
1928	*	*	£3	£6
1928 proof	*	*	*	£6
1930	*	*	£5	£8
1931	£1	£3	£8	£15
1932	£1	£3	£10	£20
1933	*	£2	£5	£10
1935	*	£5	£12	£25
1936	*	£6	£15	£30
1937	*	£2	£5	£12
1939	*	*	£3	£5
1940	*	£3	£6	£20
1941	*	£1	£3	£5
1943	*	£1	£3	£6
1944	*	£1	£3	£6
1946	*	£1	£3	£5
1949	*	£2	£5	£8
1953	*	*	£3	£5
1959	*	*	£1	£3
1966	*	*	£2	£5

DECIMAL COINAGE
50p, 10p, 5p, 2p, 1p, ½p
All issues face value only.

SETS

	F	VF	EF	Unc
1928 (in card case) ...	*	*	FDC	£120
1928 (in leather case)	*	*	FDC	£200
1966 unc. set	*	*	*	£10
1971 specimen set in folder	*	*	*	£5
1971 proof set	*	*	*	£9

113

The Anglo-Gallic Series

Chronological table of the Kings of England and France in the period 1154-1453

Henry II 1154-89
He was Duke of Normandy and Count of Anjou, Maine and Touraine. Through his marriage in 1152 with Eleanor of Aquitaine he became Duke of Aquitaine and Count of Poitou. He relinquished both these titles to his son Richard who in 1169 did homage to Louis VII of France. In 1185 he forced Richard to surrender Aquitaine and Poitou to ELEANOR who later – during Richard's absence – actually governed her provinces.

Louis VII 1137-80

Richard I (Coeur de Lion) 1189-99
After his homage to the French king, he was, in 1172, formally installed as Duke of Aquitaine and Count of Poitou. Although his father forced him in 1185 to surrender Aquitaine and Poitou to his mother he retained actual government. Later Eleanor ruled in his absence.

Philip II (Augustus) 1180-1223

John 1199-1216
He lost all provinces of the Angevin Empire except Aquitaine and part of Poitou.

Henry III 1216-72
In 1252 he ceded Aquitaine to his son Edward.

Louis VIII 1223-26
Louis IX (Saint Louis) 1226-70
Philip III 1270-85

Edward I 1272-1307
He governed Aquitaine since 1252. In 1279 he became Count of Ponthieu in the right of his wife, Eleanor of Castile. When she died in 1290 the county went to his son Edward.

Philip IV 1285-1314

Edward II 1307-27
He was Count of Ponthieu as from 1290. In 1325 he relinquished the county of Ponthieu and the Duchy of Aquitaine to his son Edward.

Louis X 1314-16
Philip V 1316-22
Charles IV 1322-28

Edward III 1327-77
He was Count of Ponthieu and Duke of Aquitaine as from 1325. At the outbreak of the war in 1337 he lost Ponthieu which was restored to him in 1360. In 1340 he assumed the title of King of France, which he abandoned again in 1360 as a result of the Treaty of Calais. He then obtained Aquitaine in full sovereignty and consequently changed his Aquitanian title from Duke (dux) to Lord (dominus) as the first one implied the overlordship of the French king. He gave Aquitaine as an apanage to his son, the Prince of Wales, better known as Edward The Black Prince, b.1330, d.1376, who was Prince of Aquitaine from 1362 till 1372, although he actually ruled from 1363 till 1371. In 1369, after war broke out again Edward reassumed the French title, which was henceforth used by the Kings of England until the Treaty of Amiens in 1802.

Philip VI (de Valois) 1328-50

John II (The Good) 1350-64

Charles V 1364-80

Richard II 1377-99
The son of the Black Prince succeeded his grandfather, Edward III, as King of England and as Lord of Aquitaine.

Charles VI 1380-1422

Heny IV 1399-1413
He adopted the same titles Richard II had, whom he ousted from the throne.

Henry V 1413-22
From 1417 until 1420 he used the title 'King of the French' on his 'royal' French coins. After the Treaty of Troyes in 1420 he styled himself 'heir of France'.

Henry VI 1422-61
He inherited the title 'King of the French' from his grandfather Charles VI. He lost actual rule in Northern France in 1450 and in Aquitaine in 1453.

Charles VII 1422-61

'All Kings of England in the period 1154-1453 had interests in France. They were Dukes or Lords of Aquitaine, Counts of Poitou or Ponthieu, Lords of Issoudun or they were even, or pretended to be, Kings of France itself, and, in those various capacities, struck coins. These coins, together with the French coins of their sons, and of their English vassals, are called Anglo-Gallic coins.'

So starts the introduction of the Bourgey-Spink book by E.R. Duncan Elias on this series. We would also like to thank Messrs Bourgey and Spink for allowing us to use some of the ilustrations from the book, as well as the chronological table of the Kings of England and France during the period.

The Anglo-Gallic Coins by E. R. D. Elias is still available from Spink and Son Ltd, London(see Some Useful Books on page 00).

Henry II
Denier,
Aquitaine

HENRY II 1152-68

	F	VF
Denier	£40	£130
Obole	£100	£280

RICHARD THE LIONHEART 1168-99
Aquitaine

	F	VF
Denier	£40	£140
Obole	£50	£150

Poitou

Denier	£35	£100
Obole	£60	£220

Issoudun

Denier		ext.rare

ELEANOR 1199-1204

Denier	£40	£120
Obole	£275	*

Edward I
Denier au lion,
during his
father's
lifetime

EDWARD I
During the lifetime of his father 1252-72

Denier au lion	£40	£130
Obole au lion	£50	£130

After succession to the English throne 1272-1307

Denier au lion	£120	£250
Obole au lion	£160	*

Edward I
Obole au lion,
after
succession

Denier á la croix longue	£100	£150
Denier au léopard, first type	£45	£90
Obole au léopard, first type	£60	£140
Denier á la couronne		ext. rare

The coinage of PONTHIEU (Northern France) under the Edwards

Edward I	F	VF
Denier	£100	£220
Obole	£120	£250
Edward III		
Denier	£130	£275
Obole		ext. rare

EDWARD II

Gros Turonus Regem		ext. rare
Maille blanche		ext. rare
Maille blanche Hibernie	£70	£175

EDWARD III 1327-77
Gold coins

Ecu d'or	£1250	£3000
Florin	£4500	£8500
Léopard d'or, 1st issue		ext. rare
Léopard d'or, 2nd issue	£1500	£3500

Edward III Léopard d'or, 2nd issue

Léopard d'or, 3rd issue	£1000	£2500
Léopard d'or, 4th issue	£1750	£4500
Guyennois d'or, 1st type	£10000	£20000
Guyennois d'or, 2nd type	£2250	£4500
Guyennois d'or, 3rd type	£1900	£3750

Silver coins

Gros aquitainique au léopard ...	£180	£490
Gros tournois à la croix mi-longue ...	£200	£550
Gros tournois à la croix longue ...	£100	£290
Sterling	£75	£250
Demi-sterling	£200	£400
Gros au léopard passant		ext. rare
Gros à la couronne	£150	£390
Gros au châtel aquitanique	£150	£390
Gros tournois au léopard au-dessus	£80	£200
Gros à la porte	£80	£200
Gros acquitanique au léopard au-dessous	£180	*
Blanc au léopard sous couronne ...	£60	£150
Gros au léopard sous couronne ...	£250	£500
Gros à la couronne avec léopard ...	£170	£400
Sterling à la tête barbue	£325	£950
Petit gros de Bordeaux		ext. rare
Gros au lion	£160	£475
Demi-gros au lion	£120	£275
Guyennois of argent (sterling)	£130	£350
Gros au buste	£700	£1500
Demi-gros au buste	£500	£1350

Black coins

Double à la couronne, 1st type ...	£100	*
Double à la couronne, 2nd type ...	£100	£200
Double à la couronne, 3rd type ...	£100	*
Double au léopard	£80	£170
Double au léopard sous couronne ...	£40	£100
Double guyennois		ext. rare
Denier au léopard, 2nd type	£35	£100
Obole au léopard, 2nd type		ext. rare
Denier au léopard, 3rd type	£45	£120
Denier au léopard, 4th type	£50	£200

THE ANGLO-GALLIC SERIES

	F	VF
Obole au léopard, 4th type	£50	£120
Denier au lion	£35	£80

N.B. Some issues of the deniers au léopard of the 2nd and 3rd type are very rare to extremely rare and therefore considerably more valuable.

The coinage of BERGERAC
Henry, Earl of Lancaster 1347-51

Gros tournois à la croix longue ...	£800	*
Gros tournois à la couronne ...	£500	*
Gros au châtel aquitainique	ext. rare	
Gros tournois au léopard au-dessus	£500	*
Gros à la couronne	£800	*
Gros à fleur-de-lis	ext. rare	
Gros au léopard passant	ext. rare	
Double	ext. rare	
Denier au léopard	ext. rare	

Henry, Duke of Lancaster 1351-61

Gros tournois à la couronne avec léopard	£600	*
Gros au léopard couchant	£700	*
Sterling à la tête barbue	ext. rare	
Gros au lion	ext. rare	

EDWARD THE BLACK PRINCE 1362-72
Gold coins

	F	VF
Léopard d'or	£950	£2000
Guyennois d'or	£1800	*
Chaise d'or	£1800	£3500
Pavillon d'or, 1st issue	£1500	£3000
Pavillon d'or, 2nd issue	£1500	£3000
Demi-pavillon d'or	ext. rare	
Hardi d'or	£1500	£3000

Edward the Black Prince Hardi d'or of Bordeaux

Silver Coins

	F	VF
Gros	£750	£1500
Demi-gros	£85	£200
Sterling	£80	£175
Hardi d'argent	£35	£95

Edward the Black Prince Hardi d'argent

Black coins

	F	VF
Double guyennois	£100	£200
Denier au lion	£50	£120
Denier	£50	£120

RICHARD II 1377-99
Gold coins

	F	VF
Hardi d'or	£1000	£2750
Demi-hardi d'or	ext. rare	

	F	VF
Silver coins		
Double hardi d'argent	£450	*
Hardi d'argent	£50	£120
Black coins		
Denier	£70	£150

HENRY IV 1399-1413
Silver coins

Double Hardi d'argent	£800	*

Henry IV Double Hardi d'argent

Hardi d'argent	£60	£120
Hardi aux genêts	ext. rare	
Black coins		
Denier	£40	£120
Denier aux genêts	ext. rare	

HENRY V 1413-22
Gold coins

	F	VF
Agnel d'or	ext. rare	
Salut d'or	£9000	£25000
Silver coins		
Florette, 1st issue	£100	£250
Florette, 2nd issue	£150	£300
Florette, 3rd issue	£70	£150
Florette, 4th issue	£70	£150
Guénar	£250	£500
Gros au léopard	£300	*
Black coins		
Mansiois	ext. rare	
Niquet	£60	£150
Denier tournois	£60	£140

HENRY VI 1422-53
Gold coins

Salut d'or	£350	£750

Henry VI Salut d'or, Dijon mint

Angelot	£1500	£3000
Silver coins		
Grand Blanc aux ècus	£40	£140
Petit Blanc	£100	£300
Trésin	ext. rare	
Black coins		
Denier Parisis, 1st issue	£60	£140
Denier parisis, 2nd issue	£60	£140
Denier tournois	£40	£130
Maille tournois	£65	£150

N.B. The prices of the saluts and grand blancs are for the mints of Paris, Rouen and Saint Lô; coins of other mints are rare to very rare and consequently more valuable.

Island Coinages

CHANNEL ISLANDS

From the date of their introduction onwards, proofs have been struck for a large number of Channel Islands coins, particularly in the case of Jersey. Except for those included in the modern proof sets these are mostly at least very rare and in the majority of cases have been omitted from the list. A number of die varieties which exist for several dates of the earlier 19th century Guernsey eight doubles have also been excluded. For further information in both cases the reader is referred to The Coins of the British Commonwealth of Nations, Part I, European Territories *by F. Pridmore, published by Spink and Son Ltd.*

GUERNSEY

	F	VF	EF	BU
TEN SHILLINGS				
1966	*	*	*	£1
THREEPENCE				
1956	*	*	*	£1
1959	*	*	*	£1
1966 proof only ...	*	*	*	£1
EIGHT DOUBLES				
1834	*	£8	£25	£100
1858	*	£8	£25	£100
1864	*	£8	£30	*
1868	*	£4	£30	*
1874	*	£4	£30	*
1885 H	*	*	£8	£25
1889 H	*	*	£6	£20
1893 H	*	*	£6	£20
1902 H	*	*	£6	£20
1903 H	*	*	£6	£20
1910 H	*	*	£8	£25
1911 H	*	*	£8	£30
1914 H	*	*	£8	£25
1918 H	*	*	£8	£30
1920 H	*	*	£4	£12
1934 H	*	*	£4	£12
1934 H prooflike ...	*	*	*	£50
1938 H	*	*	*	£5
1945 H	*	*	*	£5
1947 H	*	*	*	£4
1949 H	*	*	*	£4
1956	*	*	*	£1
1959	*	*	*	£1
1966 proof only	*	*	*	£3
FOUR DOUBLES				
1830	*	*	£20	£70
1858	*	*	£25	£80

Guernsey 1864 four doubles

	F	VF	EF	BU
1864	*	£5	£35	*
1868	*	£5	£35	*

	F	VF	EF	BU
1874	*	*	£30	*
1885 H	*	*	£8	£25
1889 H	*	*	£5	£20
1893 H	*	*	£4	£15
1902 H	*	*	£4	£15
1903 H	*	*	£4	£15
1906 H	*	*	£4	£15
1908 H	*	*	£4	£15
1910 H	*	*	£3	£15
1911 H	*	*	£3	£15
1914 H	*	*	£3	£15
1918 H	*	*	£3	£15
1920 H	*	*	*	£10
1945 H	*	*	*	£4
1949 H	*	*	*	£5
1956	*	*	*	£1
1966 proof only	*	*	*	£1
TWO DOUBLES				
1858	*	£4	£25	*
1868	*	£4	£30	*
1874	*	£4	£20	*
1885 H	*	*	£6	£15
1889 H	*	*	£4	£10
1899 H	*	*	£4	£10
1902 H	*	*	£5	£10
1903 H	*	*	£5	£15
1906 H	*	*	£4	£15
1908 H	*	*	£4	£20
1911 H	*	*	£4	£15
1914 H	*	*	£4	£18
1917 H	*	£10	£30	£60
1918 H	*	*	£2	£6
1920 H	*	*	£3	£8
1929 H	*	*	£2	£5
ONE DOUBLE				
1830	*	*	£10	£25
1868	*	£5	£20	*
1868/30	*	£5	£20	*
1885 H	*	*	£4	£10
1889 H	*	*	£2	£5
1893 H	*	*	£2	£5
1899 H	*	*	£2	£5
1902 H	*	*	£2	£5
1903 H	*	*	£2	£5
1911 H	*	*	£2	£8
1911 H new type ...	*	*	£2	£8
1914 H	*	*	£3	£8
1929 H	*	*	£1	£2
1933 H	*	*	£1	£2
1938 H	*	*	£1	£2

ISLAND COINAGES

DECIMAL COINAGE

The word 'NEW' was omitted from coins issued after December 1976, being replaced by the word for the denomination.

f denotes face value

TWENTY-FIVE POUNDS	BU
1994 50th Anniversary Normandy Landings gold	£175
1995 Queen Mother, gold, proof	£200
1996 Queen's 70th Birthday, gold, proof	£200
1996 European Football, gold, proof	£200

FIVE POUNDS
1995 Queen Mother, cu-ni	£7
1995 Queen Mother, silver, proof	£37
1996 Queen Mother's 70th Birthday, cu-ni	£7
1996 Queen Mother's 70th Birthday, silver, proof	£37
1996 European Football, cuni	£7
1996 European Football, silver, proof	£37

TWO POUNDS
1985 Liberation 40th anniversary, crown size, in blister pack	£3.45
1985 — — silver, proof	£28.75
1986 Commonwealth Games, in plastic case	£3.50
1986 — in presentation folder	£4
1986 — .500 silver, B. Unc	£15
1986 — .925 silver, proof	£28.75
1987 900th anniversary of death of William the Conqueror, cu-ni, in presentation folder	£4
1987 gold, proof	£90
1987 — silver, proof	£28.75
1988 William the Second, cu-ni in presentation folder	£4
1988 — silver, proof	£28.75
1989 Accession of Henry I cu-ni in presentation folder	£4.25
1989 — silver, proof	£28.75
1989 Royal Visit, cu-ni	£2
1989 — — in plastic case	£3.50
1989 — silver, proof	£28.75
1990 Queen Mother's 90th birthday, cu-ni	£2
1990 — — in plastic case	£3.50
1990 — silver, proof	£28.75
1991 Henry II, cu-ni	£5
1991 — — silver, proof	£30
1993 40th Anniversary of the Coronation	£28.75
1993 40th Anniversary, cu-ni	£5
1994 Normandy Landings	f
1994 — silver, proof	£30
1995 50th Anniversary of Liberations, silver, proof	£35
1995 —, silver, piedfort, proof	£60
1995 — cu-ni	£5

ONE POUND
1981 copper, zinc, nickel	£2
1981 gold proof (8 grammes)	£85
1981 gold piedfort (16 grammes)	£250
1983 new specification, new reverse	f
1985 new designs (in folder)	£1.20
1995 Queen Mother, silver, proof	£22
1996 Queen's 70th Birthday, silver, proof	£22

FIFTY PENCE
1969	£1
1970	£3
1971 proof (from set)	£5
1981	£1
1982	£1

	BU
1985 new designs	f
Other dates	f

TWENTY-FIVE PENCE
1972 Silver Wedding (cupro-nickel)	£2
1972 — proof (silver)	£8
1977 Jubilee	£1.50
1977 — silver, proof	£10
1978 Royal visit (cu-ni)	£1.50
1978 — silver, proof	£8
1980 Queen Mother's 80th birthday (cu-ni)	£1.25
1980 — silver, proof	£10
1981 Royal Wedding (cu-ni)	£1
1981 — silver, proof	£10

OTHER DECIMAL COINAGE
20p, 10p, 5p, 2p, 1p ½p. All issues face value only. *(The 5p and 10p were issued in a reduced size in 1992 and 1993 respectively.)*

SETS
1956 proof	£25
1966 proof	£8
1971 proof	£7.25
1979 proof	£8
1981 proof (including £1)	£10
1985 new designs, £1 to 1p, (7 coins)	£6
1985 — £2 Liberation crown to 1p proof (8 coins)	£25
1986 BU set in folder, £1 to 1p (7 coins)	£6
1986 £2 Commonwealth Games to 1p, proof (8 coins)	£25
1987 BU set in folder, £1 to 1p (7 coins)	£6
1987 £2 William the Conqueror to 1p, proof (8 coins)	£25
1988 BU set in folder £1 to 1p (7 coins)	£7
1988 £2 William the Second to 1p, proof (8 coins)	£25
1989 BU set in folder, £1 to 1p (7 coins)	£8
1989 £2 Henry I to 1p, proof (8 coins)	£26
1990 £2 Queen Mother's 90th birthday to 1p, proof (8 coins)	£28
1990 BU set as above (8 coins)	£10
1944 Normandy Landings, £100, £50, £25, £10 gold	£1000
1995 50th Anniversary of Liberation, £100, £50, £25, £10	£1,000
1995 Queen Mother, £25 gold, £5 silver, proof (3 coins)	£250
1995 Queen's 70th Birthday, £25 gold, £5 + £1 silver, proof (3 coins)	£250

ALDERNEY

TWENTY FIVE POUNDS
1993 Coronation, gold proof	£225

FIVE POUNDS
1995 Queen Mother, cu-ni	£7.50
1995 —, silver proof	£33
1995 — —, piedfort	£60
1995 —, gold, proof	£800

TWO POUNDS
1989 Royal Visit, cu-ni	£3
1989 — — in plastic case	£5
1989 — silver, proof	£30
1989 — — piedfort	£60
1989 — gold, proof	£800
1990 Queen Mother's 90th birthday, cu-ni	£3
1990 — in plastic case	£5
1990 — silver, proof	£30

1990 — — piedfort	... ...	£60
1990 — gold, proof	... ...	£800
1992 Accession, cu-ni	... ...	£3
1992 — —, plastic case	... ...	£5
1992 —, silver, proof	... ...	£30
1992 — —, piedfort	... ...	£60
1992 —, gold, proof	... ...	£800
1993 Coronation, cu-ni	... ...	£3
1993 — —, plastic case	... ...	£5
1993 —, silver proof	... ...	£35
1993 — —, piedfort	... ...	£60
1994 D-Day, cu-ni	... ...	£3
1994 —, card pack	... ...	£6
1994 —, silver proof	... ...	£35
1994 — —, piedfort	... ...	£60
1995 VE/Liberation, cu-ni	... ...	£3
1995 — —, plastic case	... ...	£5
1995 —, silver proof	... ...	£33
1995 —, piedfort	... ...	£60
1995 —, gold, proof	... ...	£800

ONE POUND

1993 Coronation, silver, proof	... ...	£30
1995 VE/Liberation, silver, proof	... ...	£22
1995 —, gold, proof	... ...	£300

SETS

1993 £100, £50, £25, £10, D-Day
gold, proof (4 coins) £1000
1993 £50, £25, £10, D-Day
gold, proof (3 coins) £500

JERSEY

CROWN

	F	VF	EF	BU
1966	*	*	*	£1
1966 — proof	*	*	*	£3

1/4 OF A SHILLING

	F	VF	EF	BU
1957	*	*	*	£2
1960 proof only	*	*	*	£5
1964	*	*	*	£0.30
1966	*	*	*	£0.75

1/12 OF A SHILLING

	F	VF	EF	BU
1877 H	*	*	£7	£40
1881	*	*	£9	£50
1888	*	*	£8	£40
1894	*	*	£7	£30
1909	*	*	£8	£40
1911	*	*	£5	£25
1913	*	*	£5	£20
1923	*	*	£5	£25
1923 new type	*	*	£7	£20
1926	*	*	£5	£18
1931	*	*	£2	£10
1933	*	*	£3	£10
1935	*	*	£2	£10
1937	*	*	*	£5
'1945' (George VI)[1] ...	*	*	*	£3
'1945' (Elizabeth II)[1] ...	*	*	*	£2
1946	*	*	*	£4
1947	*	*	*	£3
1957	*	*	*	£0.40
1960	*	*	*	£0.20
1964	*	*	*	£0.15
1966	*	*	*	£0.15

[1]The date 1945 on one-twelfth shillings commemorates the year of liberation from German occupation. The coins were struck in 1949, 1950, 1952 and 1954.

ISLAND COINAGES

	F	VF	EF	Unc
1/13 OF A SHILLING				
1841	*	*	£30	£100
1844	*	*	£35	£120
1851	*	*	£40	£100
1858	*	*	£35	£110
1861	*	*	£40	£100
1865 proof only	*	*	*	£350
1866	*	*	£20	£60
1870	*	*	£25	£60
1871	*	*	£25	£60
1/24 OF A SHILLING				
1877 H	*	*	£4	£30
1888	*	*	£4	£25
1894	*	*	£4	£25
1909	*	*	£3	£20
1911	*	*	£3	£20
1913	*	*	£3	£20
1923	*	*	£2	£15
1923 new type	*	*	£2	£15
1926	*	*	£2	£15
1931	*	*	£1	£5
1933	*	*	£1	£5
1935	*	*	£1	£5
1937	*	*	£1	£5
1946	*	*	£1	£5
1947	*	*	£1	£5
1/26 OF A SHILLING				
1841	*	*	£18	£75
1844	*	*	£18	£75
1851	*	*	£18	£75
1858	*	*	£18	£75
1861	*	*	£16	£65
1866	*	*	£15	£60
1870	*	*	£15	£50
1871	*	*	£18	£50
1/48 OF A SHILLING				
1877 H	*	£8	£30	£75
1/52 OF A SHILLING				
1841	*	£12	£50	£100
1841 proof	*	*	*	£300
1861 proof only	*	*	*	£400

DECIMAL COINAGE

f denotes face value

FIVE POUNDS
BU
1990 50th Anniversary of the Battle
of Britain, silver, proof... ... ... £80.50

TWO POUNDS
1981 Royal Wedding, nickel silver (crown
size) ... ... f
1981 — in presentation pack... ... ... £2.75
1981 — silver, proof £15
1981 — gold, proof... ... ... £300
1985 40th anniversary of liberation, (crown
size)... ... ... f
1985 — in presentation pack... ... ... £3.75
1985 — silver, frosted proof... ... ... £28.75
1985 — gold, frosted proof £1000
1986 Commonwealth Games £2
1986 — in presentation case... ... ... £3
1986 — .500 silver, B. Unc £14.95
1986 — .925 silver, proof... ... ... £28.75
1987 World Wildlife Fund 25 years
cu-ni in blister pack £3.25
1987 — silver, proof... ... ... £30

	BU
1989 Royal Visit cu-ni in de luxe presentation case...	£4
1989 — silver, proof...	£28.75
1990 Queen Mother's 90 birthday, cu-ni ...	£4
1990 — silver, proof	£28.75
1990 — gold, proof	..£402.50
1990 50th Anniversary of the Battle of Britain, silver, proof	£28.75
1993 40th Anniversary of the Coronation, silver, proof	£30
1995 50th Anniversary of Liberation, silver, proof	£35
1995 —, silver, piedfort, proof	£60
1996 Queen's 70th Birthday, cu-ni	£5
1996 — — — silver, proof	£33

ONE POUND

1981 cu-ni	£2.25
1981 silver, proof	£25
1981 gold, proof	£150

In 1983 Jersey issued a one pound coin with the specification changed to conform with that of the UK one pound coin. The reverse initially bore the emblem of St Helier Parish, but this was changed regularly to represent, in rotation, each of the 12 parishes of Jersey, the others being: St Saviour, St Brelade, St Clement, St Lawrence, St Peter, Grouville, St Martin, St Ouen, Trinity, St John and St Mary, in order of size of the population.

1983 new specification, new designs (both sides), on presentation card (St Helier) ...	£4
1983 silver, frosted proof, in case — ...	£23
1983 gold, frosted proof, in case — ...	£345
1984 in presentation wallet (St Saviour)	£4
1983 silver, frosted proof —	£23
1984 gold, frosted proof —	£345
1984 in presentation wallet (St Brelade) ...	£4
1984 silver, frosted proof —	£23
1984 gold, frosted proof —	£345
1985 in presentation wallet (St Clement) ...	£4
1985 silver, frosted proof —	£23
1985 gold, frosted proof —	£345
1985 in presentation wallet (St Lawrence) ...	£4
1985 silver, frosted proof —	£23
1985 gold, frosted proof —	£345
1986 in presentation wallet (St Peter) ...	£4
1986 silver, frosted proof —	£23
1986 gold, frosted proof —	£345
1986 in presentation wallet (Grouville) ...	£4
1986 silver, frosted proof —	£23
1986 gold, frosted proof —	£345
1987 in presentation wallet (St Martin) ...	£4
1987 silver, frosted proof —	£23
1987 gold, frosted proof —	£345
1987 in presentation wallet (St Ouen) ...	£4
1987 silver, frosted proof —	£23
1987 gold, frosted proof —	£345
1988 in presentation wallet (Trinity) ...	£4
1988 silver, frosted proof —	£23
1988 gold, frosted proof —	£345
1988 in presentation wallet (St John) ...	£4
1988 silver, frosted proof —	£23
1988 gold, frosted proof —	£345
1988 in presentation wallet (St Mary) ...	£4
1988 silver, frosted proof —	£23
1988 gold, frosted proof —	£345

In 1991 Jersey launched a series of six coins featuring ships built on the island during the second half of the 19th century.

1991 Silver, frosted proof 'Tickler'...	£35
1991 Gold, frosted proof 'Tickler'...	£352
1991 Silver, frosted proof 'Percy Douglas' ...	£25.80
1991 Gold, frosted proof 'Percy Douglas' ...	£352
1992 Silver, proof 'The Hebe'...	£20
1992 Gold, frosted proof 'The Hebe'	£300
1992 Silver, proof Coat of Arms	£20
1992 Gold, frosted proof Coat of Arms ...	£300
1993 Silver, proof 'The Gemini'	£30
1993 Silver, proof 'The Century'	£30
1994 silver, proof, 'The Resolute'	£25
1994 gold, proof, 'The Resolute'	£360

FIFTY PENCE

1969	£1
1983 new obv, new rev	f
1985 40th anniversary of liberation	f

TWENTY-FIVE PENCE

1977 Jubilee	£1.50
1977 — silver, proof	£17.50

TWENTY PENCE

1982 date on rocks on rev (cased)...	£0.65
1982, silver, proof, piedfort	£35
1983 new obv, with date, rev no date on rocks	f
Later dates...	f

OTHER DECIMAL COINAGE

10p, 5p, 2p, 1p, ½p (to 1982). All face value only.

1983 10p, 5p, 2p, 1p: new obv and rev designs	f
Later dates...	f

SETS

	BU
1957	£30
1960	£15
1964	£10
1966 (4 coins) proof...	£4
1966 (2 crowns)...	£7
1968/71 decimal coins	£2
1972 Silver Wedding (5 gold, 4 silver coins)	£400
1972 — — proof	£450
1972 — (4 silver coins)	£25
1980 50p to ½p	£2
1980 — frosted proof	£15
1981 £1 to ½p, in presentation pack	£3
1981 — base metal, proof	£13.95
1983 £1 to 1p (7 coins)	£3.50
1983 — silver frosted proof, in album... ...	£40
1987 £1 to 1p, in folder (7 coins)	£6
1990 50th Anniversary of the Battle of Britain, gold coins with face values of £100, £50, £25 and £10 (4 coins)	£1035
1995 50th Anniversary of Liberation, £100, £50, £25 and £10 (4 coins)	£1000

ISLE OF MAN

Contemporary forgeries of several of the earlier Isle of Man coins exist.

COPPER AND BRONZE 1709–1839

PENNIES	F	VF	EF	Unc
1709	£10	£35	£90	*
1733	*	£10	£65	£125
1733 proof	*	*	£125	£200
1733 silver	*	*	£200	£300
1758	*	£5	£50	£175
1758 proof	*	*	*	*
1758 silver	*	*	£275	£400
1786	*	£5	£40	£100
1786 plain edge proof ...	*	*	£120	£250
1798	*	£5	£45	£100
1798 bronzed proof ...	*	*	£90	£175
1798 AE gilt proof ...	*	*	£300	*
1798 silver proof	*	*	*	*

	F	VF	EF	Unc
1813	*	£5	£45	£100
1813 bronzed proof ...	*	*	£90	£175
1839	*	*	£25	£60
1839 proof	*	*	*	*

HALFPENNIES

	F	VF	EF	Unc
1709	£8	£20	£60	*
1733	*	£5	£50	£100
1733 proof	*	*	£80	£150
1733 silver	*	£60	£120	£200
1758	*	£8	£50	£120
1758 proof	*	*	*	*
1786	*	£4	£30	£65
1786 plain edge proof	*	*	£110	£200
1798	*	£5	£35	£85
1798 proof	*	*	£65	£100
1798 AE gilt proof ...	*	*	*	*
1813	*	£5	£35	£90
1813 proof	*	*	£65	£100
1839	*	*	£15	£40
1839 proof	*	*	*	*

FARTHINGS

	F	VF	EF	Unc
1839	*	£14	£18	£50
1839 proof	*	*	*	*

ISSUES SINCE 1965

Prices for the gold series, £5 to half sovereign, plus 'angels', and platinum 'nobels' are directly governed by day-to-day prices in their respective bullion markets, to which reference should be made for current valuations. Proofs have only been included in the following lists of dates if no BU coin was struck for the same year.

FIVE POUNDS
1965, 1973, 1974, 1979, 1981, 1982, 1984.

TWO POUNDS
1973, 1974, 1979, 1980 proof, 1981, 1981 Royal Wedding, 1982 Royal Birth, 1983 proof, 1984.

SOVEREIGNS
1965, 1973, 1974, 1979, 1980 proof, 1981, 1981 Royal Wedding, 1982 Royal Birth, 1983 proof, 1984, 1988.

HALF SOVEREIGNS
1965, 1973, 1974, 1979, 1980 proof, 1981, 1981 Royal Wedding, 1982 Royal Birth, 1983 proof, 1984.

ANGEL SERIES
Bullion coins in gold, introduced in 1985.
Produced in weights of 25, 20, 15, 10 and 5 ounces and 1, ½, ¼, one-tenth and one-twentieth ounce.
1991 Munich Angel, gold.
1991 Christmas Angel.

NOBLE SERIES (PLATINUM)
1985 one ounce and one-tenth ounce versions.
1986 ten ounce and five ounce versions.
1988, 1990 quarter ounce versions.

CROWNS (see also 25 pence)
1970 ... ... **£3.50**

DECIMAL COINAGE

Many basic issues for circulation in the Isle of Man have been accompanied by proofs in base metal, silver, gold and platinum, and non-proof versions in special finishes. The following lists, however, just include the basic coins or sets. Proofs in base metal are only listed if no BU coin was struck for the same year. The versions in precious metals are, in most cases, only worth their metal value, which is reflected in the day-to-day prices in their respective bullion markets.

Virenium is the trade mark of a base metal composed of 81% copper, 10% zinc and 9% nickel.

For the 50p, 10p, 5p, 2p, 1p and ½p of 1972, 1973 and 1974 mintages for each year were reported to be only 1,000 of each denomination; hence the high prices shown for these coins and the year sets in which they were included — prices which a collector could expect to pay to acquire them.

f denotes face value

FIVE POUNDS
	BU
1981 Virenium	£8
1982 — proof	£15

TWO POUNDS
1986 Virenium	f
1989 — airship on rev	f

ONE POUND
1978 Virenium	£2.50
1979, 1980 —	each £2
1981, 1982 —	f
1983, 1984, 1985, 1986 base metal, changed specification	f
1987 nickel brass, Viking design ...	f
1987 — — proof...	£4

In January 1983 the £1 coins for circulation were issued in a changed specification to conform with that of United Kingdom £1 coins. The 1983 dated coin had a reverse marking the centenary of Peel's incorporation and it was announced that reverses would be changed in three successive years to represent: Castletown (1984), Ramsey (1985) and Douglas (1986).

FIFTY PENCE
1971	*
1972, 1973, 1974	each £30
1975–78...	f

The Isle of Man frequently releases commemorative Crowns and Sets, but a full list is beyond the scope of this publication.

TWENTY PENCE
1982 cupro-nickel	*

TEN PENCE
1971	*
1972, 1973, 1974...	each £30
Later issues	f
1993 new design	f

FIVE PENCE
1971	*
1972, 1973, 1974...	each £30
Later issues	f

TWO PENCE
1971	*
1972, 1973, 1974	each £30
Later issues	f

ONE PENNY
1971	*
1972, 1973, 1974	each £30
Later issues...	f

HALF PENNY
1971	*
1972, 1973, 1974	each £30
1977 FAO	*
1984 silver...	*
Other dates	*

British Trade Tokens

British Trade Tokens were a direct response to the shortage of small denominations issued by the state. They offer the collector a fascinating insight into the life and trade of the 17th, 18th and 19th centuries.

In comparison with other collecting areas of British coins, tokens are generally speaking more affordable.

The serious collector will have to refer to the many standard books written on this subject. These are listed at the beginning of the price guide for each country.

17th century tokens

Suggested reference books:

Berry, G. (1988). *Seventeenth Century England: Traders and their tokens.* A superb book on the subject.

Boyne, W./ed Williamson, G. C. (1987–1891). *Trade Tokens issued in the Seventeenth Century* (reprinted in three volumes in 1967).

Dickinson, Michael (1986). *Seventeenth Century Tokens of the British Isles and their values.* Based on the standard reference work edited by Williamson. This book provides a full listing of 17th century tokens and gives a guide to their market value.

The Norweb Collection, Tokens of the British Isles (1575–1750), Parts I–V already published. A fully photographed record of probably the finest collection of 17th century trade tokens ever assembled. Items from the current volume are currently being offered for sale by Spink & Son Ltd.

The 17th century series issued roughly between 1648 and 1679 consists of over 17,000 known types. Mainly struck in copper and brass for local traders and borough authorities, they often identify the issuer, his/her occupation and where they lived. Collections are often based on specific counties, localities or trades.

A general value is given here for tokens of each county, depending on the rarity of the issue and these prices are those a collector can expect to pay for specimens in fine condition. Heart-shaped, octagonal and square pieces are particularly popular and being mostly rare command high prices.

Three Surrey tokens

	Common £	Scarce £	Rare £
Bedfordshire	15–30	40–60	70–200
Berkshire	15–30	40–60	80–150
Buckinghamshire	15–30	40–60	70–130
Cambridgeshire	15–30	30–60	70–110
Cheshire	—	100–150	200–400
Cornwall	50–80	100–150	200–400
Cumberland	50–80	—	300–500
Derbyshire	50–70	80–120	140–200
Devon	20–30	40–60	70–120
Dorset	20–30	40–60	70–110
Durham	30–50	60–80	90–120
Essex	15–40	60–90	100–250
Gloucestershire	15–30	40–60	70–100
Hampshire	15–30	40–60	80–150
Herefordshire	30–60	70–100	120–150
Hertfordshire	20–30	50–70	80–140
Huntingdonshire	20–30	40–50	60–100
Kent	15–30	30–50	60–150
Lancashire	—	100–150	200–400
Leicestershire	30–50	60–90	100–150
Lincolnshire	20–30	40–60	70–120
London	15–30	40–60	70–100
Middlesex	20–40	50–70	90–150
Norfolk	20–30	30–50	60–80
Northants	20–40	40–50	70–100
Northumberland	—	—	200–300
Nottinghamshire	20–40	50–60	70–110
Oxfordshire	20–30	30–40	50–90
Rutland	—	50–80	90–150
Shropshire	—	50–70	100–150
Somerset	20–30	40–50	60–80
Southwark	15–30	30–40	50–100
Staffordshire	40–60	70–90	100–140
Suffolk	20–30	40–50	70–130
Surrey	30–40	50–60	70–150
Sussex	40–50	60–70	80–140
Warwickshire	30–50	50–70	80–100
Westmorland	60–60	80–90	100–300
Wiltshire	20–30	40–50	60–90
Worcestershire	20–40	50–60	70–100

	Common	Scarce	Rare
Yorkshire	40–60	80–100	150–250
Wales	—	70–150	200–300
Isle of Man	—	—	400–500
Ireland	30–50	50–70	100–180
Scotland	—	—	300–400

	Common	Scarce	Rare
Middlesex	20–30	70–100	120–250+
Monmouthshire	20–30	50–100	100–200
Norfolk	20–30	70–100	100–200
Northamptonshire	20–30	20–40	—
Northumberland	20–50	60–100	100–150
Nottinghamshire	20–30	40–90	100–150
Oxfordshire	20–30	—	—
Rutland	—	50–100	—
Shropshire	20–30	30–60	100–150
Somerset	20–30	40–70	100–150
Staffordshire	20–30	40–70	100–200
Suffolk	20–30	50–100	100–200
Surrey	20–40	50–100	100–150
Sussex	20–30	30–60	100–150
Warwickshire	20–30	40–80	100–200+
Westmorland	20–30	50–80	100–150
Wiltshire	20–30	30–60	100–150
Worcestershire	20–40	50–100	100–150
Yorkshire	20–30	40–80	100–200
Wales	20–30	40–80	100–200
Scotland	20–30	30–60	80–150
Ireland	20–30	40–80	90–150

18th century tokens

Suggested reference books:
Dalton and Hamer. *The Provincial Token Coinage of the 18th Century* (3rd reprint 1990). A very high quality reprint by **Allan Davisson** which includes a 29 page addenda.
Schwer. *Price Guide to 18th Century Tokens.* This provides the collector with probably the most comprehensive, priced handbook ever compiled on the 18th century series as catalogued by Dalton and Hamer (1983).

Trade Tokens of the late 18th century were issued by traders and manufacturers to provide change for their customers and workers.

The Government failed to provide any copper coinage to meet the demand for small change which the industrial revolution created.

18th Century Tokens are classified as follows:
Genuine Trade Tokens: those issued by traders and manufactured to provide change for their customers and workers.
Collectors' Tokens: those issued in the 1790s for collectors, which had become a fashionable hobby in the 18th century. These are usually of superior quality depicting subjects of popular interest, or have an historical, social, or political reference.

The prices quoted in the following table are for tokens in good VF–EF condition, excluding extreme rarities. Specimens with original lustre command higher prices.

Middlesex and Norfolk Penny Tokens

	Common £	Scarce £	Rare £
Bedfordshire	20–30	40–60	
Berkshire	—	80–150	150–200
Buckinghamshire	20–40	50–100	200–300
Cambridgeshire	20–40	50–100	100–150
Cheshire	20–30	40–70	80–150
Cornwall	20–30	—	—
Cumberland	—	50–100	100–150
Derbyshire	—	50–100	200–300
Devon	20–30	40–80	100–200
Dorset	20–30	40–60	100–200
Durham	20–40	80–120	150–200
Essex	10–30	40–80	100–150
Gloucestershire	20–30	50–90	100–150
Hampshire	20–30	30–60	100–150
Herefordshire	20–40	40–60	70–100
Hertfordshire	20–30	50–90	100–150
Kent	20–30	40–80	100–150
Lancashire	20–30	50–90	100–150
Leicestershire	—	—	300+
Lincolnshire	20–30	50–100	100–150

19th century tokens

The silver token coinage

These tokens were issued mainly between 1811 and 1812 by private companies, individuals and bankers, when there was an acute shortage of official currency. In the 17th century tokens were issued exclusively by small tradesmen whereas the later examples tended to be placed into circulation by the larger manufacturers. The Industrial Revolution was changing the face and commercial structure of Britain. The most common denominations are shillings and sixpences but there are higher valued prices such as two shillings and halfcrowns.

Suggested reference books:
Dalton R. (reprinted 1968). *The Silver Token Coinage 1811–1812.*
The entire text of this book has been reprinted again by **James Mays** as a part of his interesting book, *Tokens of Those Trying Times.*
The prices quoted are for tokens in VF and EF condition, excluding rarities.

	Common £	Scarce £	Rare £
Berkshire	—	50–90	100–150
Buckinghamshire	40–80	—	—
Cambridgeshire	30–40	—	—
Cheshire	20–60	40–60	90–150
Cornwall	30–60	60–90	100–150
Derbyshire	—	60–100	100–150
Devon	20–40	50–100	100–200
Dorset	20–40	50–100	100–200
Durham	30–40	50–100	—
Gloucestershire	20–40	40–60	90–150
Hampshire	20–40	40–80	100–200
Herefordshire	30–70	—	—
Kent	—	—	90–150
Lancashire	30–30	70–100	90–150
Leicestershire	20–40	50–70	90–150
Lincolnshire	20–50	60–90	100–200
Middlesex	20–40	60–100	100–200
Norfolk	20–40	50–100	100–200
Northamptonshire	20–40	50–90	100–200
Northumberland	20–30	40–80	100–150
Nottinghamshire	20–40	40–80	90–150
Shropshire	—	—	100–200
Somerset	25–40	50–90	100–300
Staffordshire	25–40	40–70	90–150
Suffolk	—	70–150	150–250
Surrey	30–50	60–90	100–150
Sussex	20–40	50–100	110–250+
Warwickshire	20–30	50–90	100–200
Wiltshire	20–30	40–80	90–150
Worcestershire	20–30	—	—
Yorkshire	20–30	40–90	100–200
Wales	20–40	60–90	100–300
Ireland	20–50	70–100	100–200

19th century tokens also include copper pennies and halfpennies. These tokens record the country's industrial progress in the early 1800s with interesting designs depicting mills, mines, cotton works, etc.

Treasure Trove

OBJECTS of *gold or silver* whether coins, plate or bullion, which have been *hidden* in the soil or in buildings, and of which the original owner *cannot be traced* are Treasure Trove, and by law the property of the Crown. If, however, the finder of such objects reports the find promptly, and it is decided that it is Treasure Trove and therefore the property of the Crown, he will receive its *full market value* if it is retained for the Crown or a Museum. If it is not retained, he will receive back the objects themselves, with full liberty to do what he likes with them; or if he wishes it, the British Museum will sell them for him at the best price obtainable. The only way in which a finder can comply with the law and also obtain these advantages is by reporting the find promptly to the proper authority.

The proper authority is the Coroner for the District in which the find is made, for he is the authority who inquires of 'treasure that is found' and 'who were the finders' (Coroners Act 1887, section 36).

Anyone therefore who finds such objects should report the find to the Coroner, either direct or through the local Police, or by writing to the Director, British Museum, London WC1, who will communicate with the Coroner.

Coins and other ancient objects of copper, bronze, or any metal other than gold or silver are *not* Treasure Trove, and finds need not be reported to Coroners. But the British Museum is glad to hear of such finds, and if they are reported to the Director, will in suitable cases arrange for purchase or sale.

Dealers who display this symbol
are members of the

BRITISH NUMISMATIC
TRADE ASSOCIATION

All Members of the BNTA have to abide by a strict code
of ethics which is designed to protect you.

For a free Membership Directory
please send a first class stamp to the address below.

The BNTA will be organising the following
international coin fairs in 1997:

**COINEX WALES, Cardiff City Hall
18/19 April 1997**

oOo

**COINEX LONDON, Hotel Marriott, Grosvenor Sq, W1
10/11 October 1997**

oOo

For further information contact:
Mrs Carol Carter, General Secretary, BNTA
PO Box 474A, Thames Ditton, Surrey KT7 0WJ
Tel: 0181 398 4290, Fax: 0181 398 4291

THESE ARE THE CURRENT MEMBERS
OF THE B.N.T.A.
LIST OF MEMBERS IN COUNTY ORDER
(Those members with retail premises are indicated with an *)

LONDON
* A.H. Baldwin & Sons Ltd.
  Beaver Coin Room
* W. & F. C. Bonham & Sons Ltd.
* Philip Cohen Numismatics
  Chelsea Coins
  Andre de Clermont
  Michael Dickinson
* Dix Noonan Webb
* Dolphin Coins
  Christopher Eimer
* Glendining & Co.
* Knightsbridge Coins
* Lennox Gallery Ltd.
* Lubbock & Son Ltd.
  C.J. Martin Coins Ltd.
* Colin Narbeth & Son Ltd.
* George Rankin Coin Co.
* Seaby Coins/C.N.G. Inc.
  R.D. Shah
  Simmons & Simmons
  (Numismatists) Ltd.
* Spink & Son Ltd.
  Surena Ancient Art & Numismatics
* Vale Coins
* Italo Vecchi
* West Essex Coin Investments

BERKSHIRE
  Frank Milward

BUCKINGHAMSHIRE
  Europa Numismatics

CORNWALL
  Michael Trenerry Ltd.

CUMBRIA
  Patrick Finn

DORSET
  Dorset Coin Co. Ltd.

ESSEX
  E.J. & C.A. Brooks
  Mark J. Vincenzi

GLOUCESTERSHIRE
  RJB Coins

HAMPSHIRE
* SPM Jewellers
  Raymond Sleet
  Studio Coins

HERTFORDSHIRE
  KB Coins
  David Miller

KENT
  C.J. Denton
* Peter Morris

LANCASHIRE
* B.J. Dawson (Coins)
* Colin De Rouffignac
* Liverpool Medal Co
* Peter Ireland Ltd.
* R & L Coins

LINCOLNSHIRE
  Grantham Coins
  John Cummings Ltd.

MIDDLESEX
  Harrow Coin & Stamp Centre
  Ian Jull

NORFOLK
* Clive T. Dennett
  Chris Rudd

NORTHUMBERLAND
* Corbitt Stamps Ltd.

OXFORDSHIRE
  S.R. Porter

SHROPSHIRE
* Collectors Gallery

SUFFOLK
  Schwer Coins

SURREY
  G. & L. Monk

* SUSSEX
  Brighton Coin Co
  A.G. Wilson

WEST MIDLANDS
  David Fletcher-Mint Coins
* Format of Birmingham Ltd.

WORCESTER
  Whitmore

YORKSHIRE – EAST
* C.J. & A.J. Dixon Ltd.

YORKSHIRE – NORTH
* J. Smith, York

YORKSHIRE – WEST
  Airedale Coins
  Paul Clayton
  Paul Davies Ltd.

SCOTLAND
* Edinburgh Coin Shop

WALES – CLWYD
* North Wales Coins Ltd.
  C. Rumney

WALES – GWENT
* Lloyd Bennett

REPUBLIC OF IRELAND
* Coins & Medals, Dublin

COINS MARKET VALUES

BRITAIN'S MOST POPULAR NUMISMATIC ANNUAL

FOR DETAILS OF AN ADVERTISEMENT IN THE 1998 EDITION

Please call:

0181-686 2599 Ext. 473

Printed by Pensord Press Ltd, Tram Road, Blackwood, Gwent NP2 2YA